General Chemistry I
Lab Manual

Frank V. Schindler

Southwest Minnesota State University

Kendall Hunt
publishing company

Cover images © Shutterstock.com

Lightning bolt icons throughout text: © Shutterstock.com

Kendall Hunt
publishing company

www.kendallhunt.com
Send all inquiries to:
4050 Westmark Drive
Dubuque, IA 52004-1840

Copyright © 2019, 2020 by Kendall Hunt Publishing Company

ISBN: 978-1-7924-6572-7

Published in the United States of America

CONTENTS

Preface v

Laboratory Description vii

Laboratory Safety ix

Laboratory Safety Practices xiii

Laboratory Notebooks xv

Experiment 1   Measurements and Volumetric Glassware 1

Experiment 2   Introduction to Gas Chromatography and Mass Spectrometry
                (GC-MS) 23

Experiment 3   Chemistry of Household Products 35

Experiment 4   Molar Mass of an Alkali Metal Hydroxide by Titration 41

Experiment 5   Investigating Copper Reactions 49

Experiment 6   Introduction to Calorimetry 59

Experiment 7   Emission and Absorption Spectroscopy .67

Experiment 8   Synthesis and Analysis of Alum, $KAl(SO_4)_2 \cdot 12H_2O$ 77

Experiment 9   Determining the Molar Volume of Select Gases 95

Appendix 1   Notebook Example 107

Appendix 2   Common Laboratory Equipment 113

Appendix 3   Periodic Table of the Elements 117

PREFACE

Welcome to your first semester of General Chemistry Laboratory. Like many freshman chemistry students, you are likely teeming with anxiety and excitement. What student would not relish the notion of mixing reagents with anticipation of creating wonderfully interesting and colorful products or effecting effervescence, smoke, heat, sparks, or pops? Not only does this course provide an opportunity for such experiences, it exposes you to the fundamental concepts applicable to the *Science, Technology, Engineering,* and *Mathematics* (STEM) disciplines, and to everyday observation. This laboratory manual outlines experiments designed to introduce the principles and techniques of experimental chemistry with emphasis on laboratory safety, formula investigations, chemical and mathematical equation manipulation, elementary laboratory statistics, molecular drawing, and chemical reactivity. It is important to note that the experiments contained herein may not specifically correlate to any particular section(s) discussed in the lecture course, but rather, serve to augment the lecture and provide a broad range of general chemistry experience.

LABORATORY DESCRIPTION

The laboratory portion of Chemistry 231L is designed to help students better understand the material presented in the lecture portion of the class (Chem 231), and is the first laboratory course in chemistry for science majors. This course is a prerequisite for General Chemistry II laboratory (Chem 232L). Chem 231L introduces students to proper laboratory safety and quality control techniques. Students gain experience in laboratory observation, data recording and summary, drawing conclusions, and proper laboratory notebook maintenance. Although Chem 231L is closely coordinated with Chem 231, it is treated as a completely separate course carrying its own credit and grade.

Delivery of General Chemistry I Laboratory at Southwest Minnesota State University (SMSU) fosters the following SMSU Chemistry Program goals and student learning outcomes:

Goal 1. To achieve scientific competency in chemistry, across all of its subdivisions, through an ACS-approved curriculum. **Student Learning Outcome 1.1:** Demonstrate understanding of chemistry concepts.

Goal 2. To understand and apply the scientific method through an inquiry-based laboratory curriculum, culminating in independent research guided by faculty with active research programs. **Student Learning Outcome 2.1:** Apply the scientific method in laboratory situations, including competency in observation skills, hypothesis formation, experimental design, and use of proper controls.

Goal 3. To develop critical thinking skills and problem-solving techniques in course work, laboratories, and undergraduate research. **Student Learning Outcome 3.1:** Demonstrate competence in data analysis, including the preparation and interpretation of graphs and tables.

Goal 4. To understand modern chemical laboratory techniques. **Student Learning Outcome 4.1:** Demonstrate general competence in chemistry laboratory; **Student Learning Outcome 4.2:** Demonstrate competence in the use of modern chemical instrumentation.

This course requires students to maintain a laboratory notebook and complete entries for each experiment performed. The notebook is a written document formalizing: (1) the background and objectives of the experiment, (2) the materials and methods used to successfully complete the experiment, (3) the data collected, calculations performed, and observations made, (4) the results of the experiment with interpretation, speculation, and relation to the original objective(s), and (5) conclusions. Student notebooks are due one week following the completion of the laboratory experiment unless otherwise instructed. Laboratory notebook format and grading criteria are detailed in the "Laboratory Notebook" section of this manual. An example of a laboratory notebook entry is provided in Appendix 1.

LABORATORY SAFETY

 Laboratory safety is very important. Good laboratory safety practices are constantly stressed to students during their freshman chemistry courses and throughout their undergraduate education. In this course, we will handle and/or synthesize some rather obnoxious, corrosive, and potentially fatal compounds; consequently, laboratory safety must be a high priority.

The chemistry laboratory can and will be a safe place to work if all the necessary safety precautions are observed. The following paragraphs review the salient precautions needed to ensure student safety in the laboratory. Any student working in a chemistry laboratory must follow these safety rules at all times. Students who do not adhere to the stated rules will be immediately removed from the laboratory and will receive zero credit for the lab experiment in question. It is the student's responsibility to read all safety rules carefully, and then sign the safety agreement that follows.

Eye Protection: Protecting your eyes is of the upmost importance in this laboratory. Your skin in many instances can provide very short-term protection against corrosive chemicals, at least for the time needed for you to reach the emergency shower. Your eyes, however, are most susceptible to chemical damage, and once injured, are rarely salvaged. Safety goggles must be worn at all times in the General Chemistry laboratory. Prescription glasses and non-splash-proof goggles are NOT safe substitutes. Students must purchase and wear accepted splash-proof goggles similar to those sold by the SMSU Chemistry Club. Contact lenses can be a hazard due to chemical vapor dissolution and concentration behind the eye, and thus should not be worn during laboratory. Wearing prescription glasses under your safety goggles is recommended. In the event any chemical splashes near or in your eyes, immediately flush your eyes with copious amounts of water and inform your instructor. The eyewash station is one piece of laboratory equipment that should never have to be used, nevertheless, your instructor will inform of its location in the laboratory and demonstrate its use on the first day of class.

Cuts and Burns: Much of the glass tubing/rubber stopper apparatuses used in this laboratory are assembled for you, so the risk of personal injury is minimized. However, in the event you need to insert a thermometer or a glass tube into a holed rubber stopper, always do so by first lubricating the glass tubing or thermometer with glycerin, hold the tube or thermometer as close to the stopper as possible with a towel, and then insert with a twisting motion.

Be cognizant of glass temperatures when heating. Handle hot glass with wet paper towels or tongs. Never use cracked or broken glass equipment. It may ruin an experiment and worse, it may cause serious injury. Always place broken glass in the waste glass container labeled "broken glass;" never put broken glass in the garbage receptacle. First aid kits are located in every science laboratory, and are available to you should you receive a small cut or burn while working in the laboratory. Location of first aid kit is reviewed during the first class meeting.

Poisonous Chemicals: Never taste any chemicals in the laboratory. Never pipet by mouth even if you know the sample you are pipetting is water. The pipet may not have been cleaned sufficiently and contains harmful chemicals on or inside the device. Always use the fume hood and avoid breathing toxic vapors. If you are asked to sense the odor of a substance, do so by wafting a bit of the vapor toward your nose. Always wash your hands before leaving the laboratory, and before using a restroom after having completed a laboratory experiment. Eating and drinking any type of food are strictly prohibited in the laboratory. Anyone failing to adhere to this rule will be removed from the laboratory and receive zero credit for the laboratory experiment.

Clothing and Footwear: Absolutely no shorts, skirts, and/or sandals/flip-flops are allowed in the laboratory. Students who come to lab without proper clothing will be asked to leave and change into the proper attire. Long hair should be securely tied back to avoid catching fire or dangling in hazardous chemicals. If large amounts of chemicals are spilled on your body, immediately remove the contaminated clothing and use the safety shower. Make sure to inform your instructor about the problem. Place your coats and backpacks in the cubbies provided. Do not leave them on the floor for someone to trip over.

Fire: In case of fire or an accident, inform your instructor at once and then leave the laboratory. Do not try to use the fire extinguishers yourself.

Laboratory Care and Waste Disposal: Your instructor is NOT your mother. Please be sure to leave the equipment and all workspaces as you found them. At the end of the each lab session, clean off your work area, and wash all glassware and miscellaneous equipment. When massing any material on the balances, do not weigh directly onto the balance pan. Weigh your material on a piece of massing paper. The balances are very sensitive and expensive instruments and should be treated with great care. It is imperative all chemicals spilled on or near the balance be cleaned up immediately. If the instructor finds chemical spills and/or open chemical containers at or near the balances at the completion of the laboratory, all students will lose points on their lab report.

Never put excess reagents back into the bottle from which they came. The reagent(s) may be contaminated, and you run the risk of contaminating the entire reagent container. Treat the excess as recovered chemicals and place it in the recovered chemicals container labeled "hazardous waste" located in the fume hood. Be sure to dispose of all recovered chemicals generated during the course of an experiment in the recovered chemicals container located in the fume hood. Never flush recovered chemicals down the drain unless specifically told to do so by your instructor. Your instructor will also demonstrate how to correctly open and transfer reagents from a reagent bottle as to reduce the risk of spillage, contamination, and/or injury.

The instructor will go over the "Laboratory Safety Practices" that follow, and each student must read, sign, date, and submit the form before working in the laboratory.

LABORATORY SAFETY PRACTICES

The laboratory is a safe working place when precautions and proper techniques are employed. Your safety practices are as important to your instructor and the University as they are to you, and your attention to safety or lack thereof can and will directly affect your laboratory partner and/or fellow students. Most precautions are just common-sense practices. These include the following:

1. Wear splash-proof safety goggles at all times while in the laboratory.
2. Wear shoes at all times. No open-toed shoes.
3. No shorts, skirts, or low-cut apparel.
4. Long hair should always be tied back to minimize the chances of starting on fire from Bunsen burners or dangling in chemicals.
5. Eating, drinking, and smoking are strictly prohibited in the laboratory at all times.
6. No horseplay in the laboratory.
7. Know where to find and how to use safety and first aid equipment.
8. Consider all chemicals to be hazardous unless you are instructed otherwise.
9. If chemicals come in contact with your skin or eyes, wash immediately with large amounts of water and then report it to your laboratory instructor.
10. Never taste anything. Never directly smell the source of any vapor or gas; instead, and only if necessary, gently waft the vapors toward your nose from a safe distance.
11. Always use a pipet bulb when drawing solution into pipet; *Never* pipet by mouth!
12. Any reactions involving skin irritating or hazardous chemicals, or unpleasant odors, are to be performed in the fume hood.
13. Never point a test tube that you are heating at yourself or your neighbor since it may splatter out of the opening.
14. No unauthorized experiments are to be performed in the laboratory.
15. Clean up all broken glassware immediately.
16. Always pour acid into water, NOT water into acid, because the heat of solution will cause the water to boil and the acid to splatter. For the same reason, always pour concentrated reagent solutions into diluted reagent solutions.
17. Avoid rubbing your eyes unless you are sure your hands are clean.

18. When inserting glass tubing or thermometers into rubber stoppers, lubricate the tubing and the hole in the stopper with glycerin. Wrap the tubing in a towel and grasp the tubing as close to the end being inserted as possible. Slide the tubing into the rubber stopper with a twisting motion. DO NOT PUSH. Keep your hands as close together as possible to reduce the leverage. Finally, remove excess lubricant by wiping with the towel.

19. Notify your instructor immediately in case of an accident.

20. Comply with all special precautions mentioned in your experiments and with all special directions emphasized by your instructor.

21. Never use any chemical found in an unlabeled container.

22. Many common organic reagents such as alcohols, acetone, and ether are highly flammable. Do not use them anywhere near an open flame.

23. Read the reagent bottle label twice to be certain that it is the chemical you want. The label of the reagent will list content's purity and safety hazards. If there is no indication of safety hazards of the chemical, treat it as though it is flammable, volatile, and poisonous until you have checked the Material Safety Data Sheet (MSDS) for the chemical.

24. Never work alone in the laboratory.

My signature indicates that I have read, understood, and will do my best to comply with these safety rules.

NAME (please print): _____

SIGNATURE: _____

DATE: _____

LABORATORY NOTEBOOKS

The purpose of the laboratory notebook is to record all work performed in the laboratory in a complete, orderly, and chronological fashion. The notebook provides a complete and accurate account of your work, and enables others to repeat, if necessary, exactly what you did in efforts to obtain the same results. The instructions that follow closely resemble the maintenance requirements of a typical commercial or research laboratory notebook, and are designed to ensure a complete legal record of work performed. The details as outlined closely reflect the proper maintenance of the typical paper laboratory notebook (PLN), but should also be observed for the electronic laboratory notebooks (ELNs) described later. An example of a laboratory experiment properly entered into a PLN is included in Appendix 1.

1. Save the first three or four pages for a "Table of Contents" unless a table of contents area is already provided within the notebook. The table of contents should include the title of each experiment and its page number, and other pertinent information. No numbered pages are to be removed from the notebook. **Original pages must NOT be removed from the notebook**. This description pertains to PLNs only.

2. Notebooks should have a preface, a short explanation of who the author is, the purpose of the notebook or goal of the work, and where the work is being conducted. The purpose of the notebook may be abundantly clear to you as the author, but may not be so clear to others. By providing a preface, future readers will understand why the notebook was maintained. Figure 1 shows an example of a student preface.

3. If using a PLN, all entries in the notebook *must be in ink* and *clearly legible*. The notebook is not intended as a work of art, but it should be reasonably neat. Your instructor becomes more irritated with "flawless" notebooks than those with mistakes lined through. A flawless notebook often indicates the analyst wrote down everything in a separate notebook and then later transcribed all information to their laboratory notebook in effort to eliminate all grammatical errors and make the entries aesthetically pleasing. This is a no-no! All information should be entered directly into the notebook.

4. The notebook is divided into sections for each experiment. At the start of each experiment, write the date and title of the experiment. Immediately below this information, write the "Introduction" or "Purpose" describing the nature of the experiment to be performed. This is important so that someone reading the notebook can obtain an overview of the purpose of the experiment and understand the

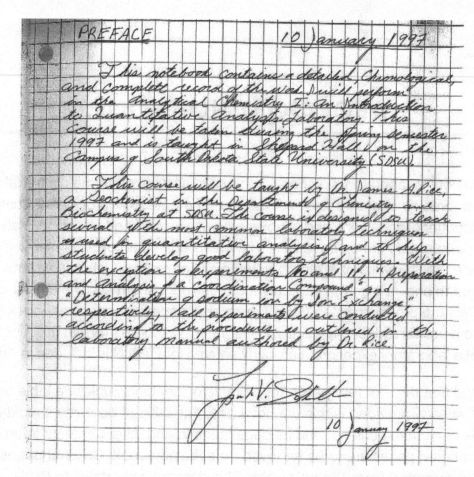

FIGURE 1   Preface to a notebook used by a student to record laboratory experiments in quantitative analysis.

significance of the data entries that follow. The introduction should start with an explanation and support of the experiment. Why is the experiment being performed? What related work has been done, and what were the results? This may require you to search the literature and cite specific references. All pertinent chemical reactions, and chemical and structural formulas related to the experiment should be included in this section. The "Introduction" should close with the specific objectives of the experiment.

5. You should include a "Materials and Methods" or "Procedures" section after the introduction. Include a brief listing of the materials used and safety concerns. This section specifically describes the work performed. Also, list the general form of any equation(s) used in calculating your results.

6. Following the experimental section, include a "Data and Observation" section. Data must be complete and entered directly in the notebook as they are obtained. For example, a massing should be entered directly in the notebook, NOT copied from a scratch paper. When errors are made or data are discarded for any reason, neatly place a line through the erroneous notebook entry and write a brief explanation as to why the entry was rejected. Initial all data changes. All data must be adequately labeled so that they

are intelligible to a chemist unfamiliar with the work. It is not necessary to write a detailed discussion of the principles involved, but it should be clear exactly what was done and why. Therefore, each data entry should be preceded by a statement, which clearly identifies it and explains its relationship to the experiment being performed. Constructing a data table with title facilitates this requirement. *All measurements related to mass must be recorded in the data section and include all tare, gross, and net masses. Likewise, all measurements related to volume (i.e., graduated cylinder, and/or burets) must be recorded in the data section and include all initial, final, and net volume readings.*

This section is a very important part of your notetaking, because you record the observations you make during the course of the experiment. All important observations bearing on the experiment should be entered. For example, if a sample splatters during evaporation or a filter paper ignites when placed in an oven, this must be noted in your records. Any irregularity such as a discolored precipitate or a fading end-point or an unstable measuring instrument must be recorded. This information is important in evaluating the reliability of data and sometimes is used as justification for rejection of questionable experimental data.

7. Include a "Calculation" section where you show an example of each type of calculation used. For example, if your experiment requires three trials or replicate determinations, show all associated calculations for one trial. It is not necessary to show the complete calculation of ALL trials. You can simply summarize the remaining results in the "Results" section.

8. Include a "Results and Discussion" section where you summarize your results in a table format, and reflect on what you did and what you observed during the course of the experiment. This section is where you construct tables, graphs, and any other illustrations to provide a clear understanding of representative data obtained from the experiment. Here you interpret your results and relate them to the objectives of the experiment. Discuss relationships, generalizations, shortcomings, and difficulties of the experiment. Discussions should focus on the meaning of your findings, not to recapitulate them. This section is where you should answer questions asked in the laboratory handout. Your discussion is used to "understand" the results. Do the results support your hypothesis or refute it? Speculation(s) are made in this section.

9. Provide a "Conclusions" section. Conclusions summarize the goal of your experiment, what was performed, and what was found. Was the goal achieved, and/or objectives satisfied? Was the hypothesis supported? Conclusions put interpretations into the context of the original problem. This section should be brief.

10. You must have your notebook whenever working in the lab. If using a PLN, it is generally best not to leave it in your lab drawer, because acid fumes from samples stored there may cause the paper to deteriorate and the notebook to fall apart.

11. Within each section, all entries must be made in chronological sequence. Enter the date at the start of each day's work. On completion of that day's work, sign the page at the end of the data and again write the date. *Then have your instructor*

initial below your signature as a "witness." At the start of the next laboratory period, enter the date, and then start entering data where you left off the previous period. Do not leave large spaces between dated entries.

This course will use ELNs. An ELN is a computer program designed to replace PLNs. ELNs allow students to record, organize, summarize, and report laboratory experimentation. Students will use their laptops with Microsoft OneNote® to access and maintain their ELN. Students may choose to use the OneNote® 2016 version if available, because it provides functionality similar to Microsoft Word® and Microsoft Excel®, and therefore makes entering equations and graphical information into the ELN easy. Otherwise, students will create equations in Microsoft Word® and then copy and paste the equations into OneNote®. Alternatively, students may use the "alt =" command to insert an equation box directly into OneNote® and then commence using Equation Editor shortcut commands. Students will also use Microsoft Excel® to satisfy all graphing requirements. Students must have an Office 365 organizational account, and use Microsoft Edge®, Mozilla Firefox®, or Goggle Chrome® to access the full version of OneNote online.

Figure 2 shows a screen shot of a student's OneNote® notebook screen. Note the "sections" are listed left-hand side of the screen. The Sections for Chem 231L are Preface,

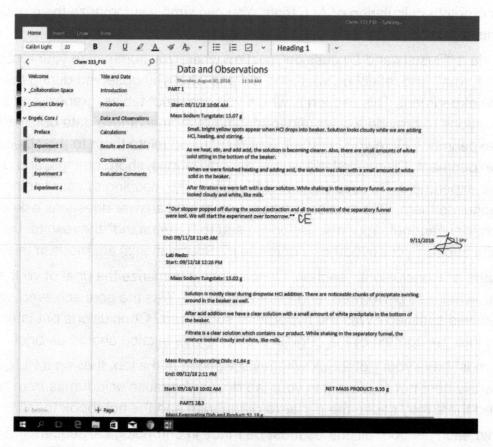

FIGURE 2   A screen shot of a student's OneNote® notebook showing part of the "Data and Observation" page of the "Experiment 1" section. © *Cora J. Engels*

Experiment 1, Experiment 2, etc. Within each Section are "Pages." The Pages for Chem 231L are "Title and Date," "Introduction," "Procedures" or "Materials and Methods," "Data and Observations," "Calculations," "Results and Discussion," and "Conclusions." An added page titled "Evaluation Comments" or "Evaluation Rubric" is included with each experimental section. This page is reserved for the instructor's evaluation of the student notebook according to the grading rubric in Table 1. The OneNote® notebooks will be created in advance, and once the instructor adds the student to notebook roster, he/she will receive an email with a notebook link that provides student access to the notebook.

As part of the ELN, students will use Advanced Chemistry Development, Inc., or ACD/ChemSketch® molecular drawing software. ACD/ChemSketch® freeware is for academic and personal use, and is a drawing package that allows you to draw chemical structures including organics, organometallics, polymers, and Markush structures. It also includes features such as 3D molecular viewing and molecular optimization. Students are allowed one individual installation and can access the free download from http://www.acdlabs.com/resources/freeware/chemsketch/. Students are expected to use ACD/ChemSketch to draw structural formulas of compounds and paste them into their ELN.

Unless instructed otherwise, ELNs will be due one week following the completion of the laboratory experiment. Notebooks will be evaluated according to the grading criteria outlined Table 1.

TABLE 1   Grading rubric for Experimental Notebook.

Item	Points Possible
Notebook preface, experiment title, date, and analyst's name	1
Introduction: includes objectives, chemical reactions, and chemical and structural formulas	3
Procedures: includes materials and safety concerns, and equation(s) used in calculating results	3
Data and Observations well labeled, understandable, and complete. All data acquisition entered in notebook with proper laboratory start and stop dates, times, and signatures; section includes witness signature.	4
Calculations: Complete with example of each type	3
Results and Discussion: Results tabulated; appropriate figures, tables, and illustrations provided; Results interpreted and related to objectives	4
Conclusions: summarized the goal of your experiment, what was performed, and what was found; interpretations into the context of the original problem	2
Total	**20**

Measurements and Volumetric Glassware

INTRODUCTION

Laboratory Measurements

Chemistry is an exact science and thus requires precise, accurate measurements of length, volume, mass, temperature, etc. Measuring mass and volume in general chemistry is routine. Chemical analyses are only as accurate as the measurements recorded during the analytical procedure. One cannot expect accurate, precise analytic results if one or more data measurements are inaccurate. In addition, an understanding of when high degree of accuracy is

| Accurate and precise (a) | Precise, not accurate (b) | Not accurate, not precise (c) |

Source: Frank Schindler

needed and when only estimated quantities are needed is very important in the chemistry laboratory. For instance, if a student uses a beaker to prepare a standard reagent instead of a volumetric flask, significant errors in the accuracy of the student's results are likely. Conversely, there is no point in measuring masses and/or volumes of reagents to a high degree of accuracy if the experiment is purely qualitative and only requires approximate amounts.

Significant figures. Every measurement made in the laboratory contains a certain amount of uncertainty. The uncertainty of any measurement results from a combination of both the person and the instrument used in making the measurement. Any number used to record a laboratory measurement should indicate the degree of uncertainty. For example, if a student measures the mass of a solid material on a centigram balance and records the mass as 2.89 g, this mass would indicate an uncertainty in the hundredths (0.01) of a gram. That is, 2.89 g would represent an uncertainty in the second decimal place or a mass uncertainty of ± 0.01 g. We can represent this fact as 2.89 ± 0.01 g, but it is generally recognized that the uncertainty is in the second decimal place and the "± 0.01 g" is left off.

In the value 2.89 g, the 2 and the 8 are certain digits, while the 9 is the one uncertain digit. All certain digits and one uncertain (estimated) digit are called **significant figures** or significant digits. Thus, 2.89 g contains three significant figures. Likewise, a length of 1.5 cm would have an uncertainty of ± 0.1 cm, would represent either 1.4 cm or 1.6 cm, and contains two significant figures (one certain value, "1," and one uncertain value, "5"). *The last digit of any measured value is always considered uncertain or estimated and should be included as a significant figure.* Zeros can create confusion when determining the amount of significant figures. The general rules for zeros are as follows and are transcribed directly from Brown et al. (2015):[1]

1. Zeros *between* nonzero digits are always significant—1005 kg (four significant figures; 1.03 cm (three significant figures).

2. Zeros *at the beginning* of a number are never significant; they merely indicate the position of the decimal point—0.02 g (one significant figure); 0.0026 cm (two significant figures).

3. Zeros *at the end* of a number are significant if the number contains a decimal point—0.0200 g (three significant figures); 3.0 cm (two significant figures).

4. Zeros *at the end* of a number may or may not be significant if the number does not contain a decimal point. For example, 200 g may contain one, two, or three significant figures, but since there is no decimal point, it would normally be assumed to contain only one significant figure, i.e., the two zeros to the right of "2" would not be considered significant. To eliminate any confusion, always use scientific notation when expressing the correct level of significance for such a value—2×10^2 (one significant figure); 2.0×10^2 (two significant figures); 2.00×10^2 (three significant figures). Note that the coefficient in scientific notation always indicates the number of significant figures.

When making calculations involving significant figures, the following rules apply:[1]

1. *Multiplication and division*: the result contains the same number of significant figures as the measurement with the fewest significant figures (i.e., the least precise measurement). For example:

$$\text{Area} = l \times w = (6.221 \text{ cm}) (5.2 \text{ cm}) = 32.3492 \text{ cm}^2 = 32 \text{ cm}^2 \qquad (1.1)$$

2. *Addition and subtraction*: the result contains the same number of decimal places as the measurement with the fewest decimal places. For example:

Perimeter (*P*) of rectangle is equal to the sum of four sides =
width + width + length + length

$$P = 5.2 \text{ cm} + 5.2 \text{ cm} + 6.221 \text{ cm} + 6.221 \text{ cm} = 22.842 \text{ cm} = 22.8 \text{ cm} \qquad (1.2)$$

3. Exact numbers have no uncertainty associated with them, and are derived from defined relationships or are a result of counting. Exact numbers are NOT used to determine the amount of significance of a calculated value. For example:

$$22.8 \text{ cm} \left(\frac{1 \text{ in.}}{2.54 \text{ cm}} \right) \left(\frac{1 \text{ ft}}{12 \text{ in.}} \right) = 0.7480315 \text{ ft} = 0.748 \text{ ft} \qquad (1.3)$$

The significance of this calculated result, i.e., 0.748 ft is determined from the initial measured value of 22.8 cm, not the factors used in its conversion.

Volume Measurements. There is a variety of volume-measuring devices used in the chemistry laboratory with a range of accuracies. Students must be able to discern when highly accurate or only approximate volumes of liquid reagents are needed to adequately complete the chemistry experiment. For instance, there is no point in using a pipet when a graduated cylinder will do, and one would not use a graduated cylinder when the accuracy of a pipet is required. Likewise, one should not use a beaker to deliver 10.5 mL of a liquid reagent, nor would one ever bring a standard reagent to volume in a beaker. The volumetric glassware used in this course includes volumetric flasks, pipets (two types), graduated cylinders, burets, and beakers (Fig. 1.1).

The *volumetric flask* (Fig. 1.1A) is the most accurate volume-measuring device in chemical laboratories. They are calibrated to contain a specific volume of a solution at a specified temperature, usually 20°C. An etched ring in the neck of the flask indicates the level of the bottom of the meniscus of the solution in the flask when it contains the calibrated volume.Note that the volumetric flask is calibrated "to contain" (TC) not "to deliver" (TD) a specified volume of solution. Consequently, if the contents of a volumetric flask are emptied into a receiving vessel, LESS than the calibrated volume is delivered, because a small amount of the liquid remains on the walls of the flask. Volumetric flasks are used for dilution of sample solutions in order to ascertain an accurate volume, and thus an accurate concentration.

Volumetric pipets (Fig. 1.1B) are the most accurate (within 0.1% of calibrated value) device for delivering a measured volume of solution. A volumetric pipet is calibrated to deliver an accurate, single volume whereas a Mohr pipet (Fig. 1.1C) can deliver a range of volumes, e.g., 0–5 or 0–10 mL, in various increments. Because the volumetric or transfer pipets are calibrated at a specified temperature to deliver an accurate volume of solution, the pipets contain slightly more solution when filled to the calibration mark then they actually deliver.

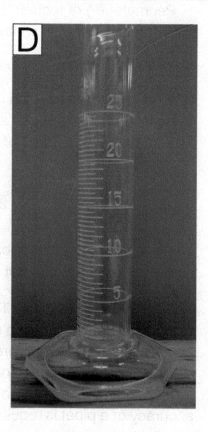
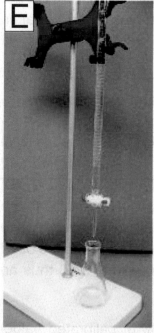

FIGURE 1.1   Various volumetric glassware used in General Chemistry laboratory. Volumetric flask (A), volumetric pipet (B), Mohr pipet (C), graduated cylinder (D), buret (E), graduated beaker (F). *Source: Frank Schindler*

As with any piece of glassware, never assume it is clean. Always clean the pipet with hot water and lab soap, rinse with hot top water, and then perform a final rinse with distilled water (at least 3x). Always condition the pipet by rinsing it several times with small amounts of the sample to be delivered. Once cleaned and conditioned, draw the sample solution into the pipet using a pipet bulb (NEVER USE YOUR MOUTH!) well beyond the calibration mark and then quickly remove the pipet bulb and seal the pipet end with your forefinger. Gently release the seal made by your finger until the lower edge of the meniscus aligns with the etched calibration mark located on the upper stem of the pipet. The calibrated volume is allowed to drain completely via gravity into the receiving vessel. The drop at the tip of the pipet is then touched off by bringing the tip in contact with the wall of the receiving vessel. A small amount of solution will be present in tip of the pipet; this is normal and the small amount of remaining liquid should NEVER be blown out. Figure 1.2 illustrates the proper use of a volumetric pipet.

A *buret* (Fig. 1.1E) is a graduated volume-measuring device capable of incremental volume delivery of solution. The buret is similar to a Mohr pipet, but it is much more accurately calibrated and its flow is carefully controlled by use of a stopcock. Consequently, burets are used in titrations where careful control of the stopcock allows for accurate titrant delivery and end-point determination. Burets are first cleaned with a detergent and buret brush, rinsed with distilled water, and then conditioned with titrant. Burets are filled with titrant and then allowed to drain into a waste beaker until the lower edge of the meniscus is below the zero mark. This eliminates any air bubbles trapped in the buret tip that would affect the volume measurement. Allow a minute or so for the meniscus to stabilize, and then record the initial buret reading. Since we are only interested in the net titrant volume (i.e., the difference between the initial and final buret reading, also referred to as the *titre*), it is not necessary and is a waste of time trying to align the meniscus to read exactly 0.00 mL. *Initial and final buret readings should always be recorded in the laboratory notebook.*

All buret readings should be read to the nearest 0.01 mL, with the final digit being an estimated and thus uncertain digit. In reading a buret, first determine the *scale increment*. To find the scale increment, subtract the values of any two adjacent labeled graduations and divide by the number of intervals between them. For example, in Fig. 1.3, the labeled graduations are 14 and 15 mL. So, subtract 15 mL − 14 mL = 1 mL and divide by the number of intervals between them, which in this case is = 10. Therefore, the scale increment for the buret in Fig. 1.3 is equal to 1.0 mL 10 graduations^{-1} = 0.10 mL graduation^{-1}. The buret should be read to one digit beyond the scale increment, i.e., to 0.01 mL. Based on the scale increment, the volume of the buret reading in Fig. 1.3 = 14.05 ± 0.01 mL. Note the reading contains two certain values, i.e., 14 and 0.0 mL. The "0.0 mL" is determined from the fact the meniscus lies between the two graduations below the labeled graduation of 14, thus, 0 graduations × 0.1 mL graduation^{-1} = 0.0 mL. The certain values are 14 + 0.0 = 14.0 mL. The one uncertain value, i.e., 0.05 mL, is obtained by noting the meniscus lies approximately halfway between the 14.0 and 14.1 graduations.

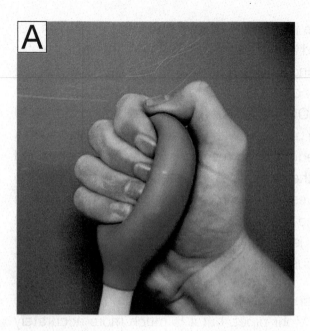

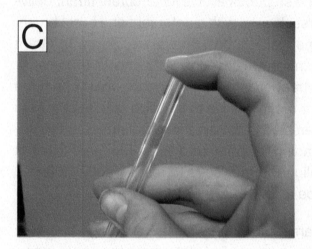

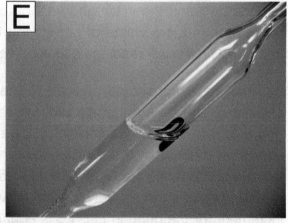

FIGURE 1.2   Filling and dispensing solution from a volumetric pipet. Squeeze bulb and place it on end of pipet (A), draw solution into pipet beyond calibration mark (B), remove bulb and seal end of pipet with index finger (C), slightly release seal by twisting middle finger, ring finger, and thumb simultaneously (C), and then allow solution to drain until meniscus becomes aligned with calibration mark (D), allow pipeted volume to drain completely into the receiving vessel (E) making sure to touch any remaining droplets of solution onto the inside wall of the receiving vessel. Do not remove the small amount of solution remaining in the tip of the pipet. *Source: Frank Schindler*

FIGURE 1.3   A typical buret with buret card (positioned behind the buret) showing a volume of 14.05 ± 0.01 mL. Note that burets are always read from top to bottom and at eye level or at a 90° angle to avoid parallax error. The difference in initial and final reading equals the net volume of delivered solution. *Source: Frank Schindler*

Consequently, the final reading is 14 + 0.0 + 0.05 = 14.05 mL, which corresponds to four significant values in this reading.

Burets are read to two decimal places with the 0.01 mL position representing the estimated or uncertain yet significant value. In addition, burets should always be read at eye level or at a 90° angle to avoid parallax error. Parallax error occurs when you read the volume of the liquid at a height either higher or lower than your eye level.

It is recommended students fabricate and use a *buret card* (Fig. 1.3) to assist in reproducing titrant volumes and increasing precision. A buret card is made by making a black, horizontal streak on a white notecard with a felt-tipped marker. The buret card is then placed behind the buret with the upper limit of the black streak placed just under the meniscus, so that the bottom of the meniscus can be seen distinctly against a narrow zone of white.

Graduated cylinders (Fig. 1.1D) are also used to measure a liquid volume, are calibrated either "to contain" (TC) or "to deliver" (TD), and are available in many different sizes. The measurement accuracy of a graduated cylinder is less than that of either the buret or volumetric pipet, so students must consider the desired accuracy before choosing to use a graduated cylinder. Expected accuracies of volumes measured are typically in the range of 1–2% of the volume of the cylinder.[2] For example, measurement of 50 mL of solution with a 500-mL graduated cylinder should be accurate within 5 or 10 mL. Generally, graduated cylinders are not appropriate for the preparation of standard solutions, i.e., pipets, volumetric flasks, and burets should be used in this instance.

Like the buret, graduated cylinders are read by first determining the scale increment. To find the scale increment, subtract the values of any two adjacent labeled graduations and divide by the number of intervals between them. Unlike the buret, however, graduated cylinders are read from bottom to top. Figure 1.4 shows two typical graduated cylinder readings.

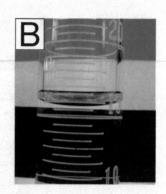

FIGURE 1.4   Example graduated cylinder volume readings. A 100-mL graduated cylinder will a scale increment = 1 mL graduation^{-1} and a volume reading = 24.8 ± 0.1 mL (A). A 25-mL graduated cylinder with a scale increment = 0.5 mL graduation^{-1} and a volume reading = 15.55 ±0.05 mL. *Source: Frank Schindler*

Beakers (Fig. 1.1F) should not be considered volumetric glassware because of their inaccuracy (e.g., as much as 10% error).[2] The graduated markings on beakers are only useful for rough volume measurements, and consequently, beakers are typically used only for bulk mixing and/or as solution holding vessels. Beakers should NEVER be used as the volume-measuring device in making up standard solutions of accurate concentration.

Most laboratory glassware is either Pyrex® or Kimax®, registered trademarks of Corning and Kimble Chase, respectively, and are made from borosilicate glass possessing low coefficients of thermal expansion. Despite the low thermal expanding properties, the volume of borosilicate glassware can change slightly with every degree change in temperature. Consequently, if your application requires accurate measurements and a certain level of reliability on the graduations printed on the glassware, volumes need to be measured as close to the glassware's calibration temperature as possible. Calibration temperatures are usually printed on the glassware itself.

Mass Measurements. *Mass* is a measurement of the amount of matter in an object, whereas *weight* is a measurement of gravitational force acting on an object and is a function of the distance from the center of earth, i.e., the apparent weight of an object becomes less further from the earth's surface. The mass of a particular object remains constant, but the object's weight can vary depending on where the measurement is taken in relation to the earth's gravitational pull. In this laboratory, student should refrain from using the term "weight" and use the more correct "mass" term.

There are several types of mass measuring devices or balances used in the general chemistry laboratory, each of which having a finite, but inherent level of sensitivity (Fig. 1.5). For instance, the *triple-beam* balance (Fig. 1.5A) is the least sensitive and is used when reagents or samples need to be massed only approximately (to the nearest 0.1 or 0.01 g).

The *top-loading* balances (Fig. 1.5B) typically possess intermediate sensitivity and can accurately mass objects with masses of up to 300 g and to two or three decimal places, i.e., to 0.01 or 0.001 g (1 mg), respectively. This balance is very susceptible to air currents and balance level at a sensitivity of 0.001 g; therefore, top-loading balances are typically used at 0.01 g sensitivity unless fitted with some type of screen to eliminate the effect of air currents.

The most accurate mass-measuring device used in the chemistry laboratory is the *analytical* balance (Fig. 1.5C). The analytical balance has high sensitivity and can mass an object to the nearest 0.0001 g. That is, a sample mass = 0.2345 g would contain four significant figures and would have a measurement uncertainty of ±0.0001 g. The analytical balance is very delicate and must be handled carefully, used correctly, and not abused.

Objects in the chemistry lab can be massed two different ways. A *direct massing* (determining the absolute mass) is accomplished by zeroing the balance, placing the object on the balance, and obtaining the mass from the balance reading. The second method is called *massing by difference*, where a beaker or massing paper is placed on the balance and massed (tare mass). The object is then placed in the beaker or on the paper

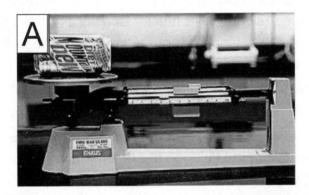

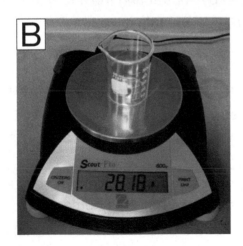

FIGURE 1.5   Examples of balances used in mass measurements. Triple-beam balance (A); electronic top-loading balance (B); electronic analytical balance (C). *Source: Frank Schindler*

and the mass of the object plus the container is recorded (gross mass). The mass of the object or sample (net mass) is determined by subtracting the tare mass from the gross mass. The advantage of this method is that any error in the zero setting on the balance will affect both massings equally and the net mass (mass of sample) will be obtained correctly.

A common error in massing is the lack of temperature equality between the sample being massed and the balance. When temperatures are not equilibrated, convection currents may set up within the balance causing an error of a few tenths of a milligram or more.[2] If the sample mass appears to "drift" with time, it is usually the result of the gradual equilibration of temperatures between the balance and the sample being masses or it could be a hygroscopic sample readily adsorbing moisture from the air. Nonetheless, any sample dried in the oven should always be placed in a desiccator to effect complete temperature equilibration prior to massing.

A brief outline of massing procedures is given below.[2]

A. Massing into a beaker or flask:

1. Zero the balance, place a clean, dry flask or beaker (sample container) on the balance (make sure the sample container does not exceed the mass capacity of the balance), close the balance doors, and measure the mass (record as **tare mass** in your notebook).

2. Calculate the total (**gross**) mass of the sample container plus sample by mentally adding the desired sample mass to the tare mass.

3. Using a clean spatula, tap enough sample to bring the gross mass to approximately the required value. Close the balance doors and obtain the accurate mass (record as gross mass in your notebook).

4. Determine the sample mass (net mass) by subtracting the tare mass from the gross mass. Make sure to record all measurements in your notebook.

B. Massing from a massing bottle:

1. Zero the balance and then mass the massing bottle containing the sample.

2. Grasp the massing bottle by using a strip of paper wrapped around it. Tilt the bottle over the sample container and tap the side of it with a spatula so that some sample falls into the container.

3. Return the massing bottle to an upright position and again tap the side so that sample falls back into the bottom. Remass the massing bottle.

4. Subtract the final mass of the massing bottle plus sample (tare mass) from the original mass (gross mass) to get the net mass of sample transferred to the container. Repeat steps 2 and 3 as required to get sufficient sample into the beaker.

C. Massing by the direct method (or determining the absolute mass):

1. Place a sample container on the balance and then zero. Note: Always use a sample container or massing paper. Never place a sample directly on the balance pan.

2. Place the sample or object in the container or on the massing paper and measure its mass.

D. Massing on Massing paper

1. Zero the balance, place creased massing paper on the balance, calculate the total (gross) mass of the massing paper plus sample by mentally adding the desired sample mass to the paper mass.

2. Using a clean spatula, tap enough sample to bring the gross mass to approximately the required value. Close the balance doors and obtain the accurate mass. This should be recorded in your notebook as the **gross mass**.

3. Quantitatively transfer the sample from the paper to the receiving vessel being careful to affect complete transfer without sample loss.

4. Zero the balance, place the creased massing paper on the balance, close the balance doors, and record the paper mass. This should be recorded in your notebook as the **tare mass**. This mass accounts for any small amount of sample that may remain on the paper after sample transfer.

5. Determine the sample mass (**net mass**) by subtracting the tare mass from the gross mass.

Statistical Analyses

Accuracy and *precision* are statistical parameters of particular interest to an analyst. The accuracy of a determination refers to how close a measurement comes to an accepted or true or most probable value. Precision refers to how much variation exists in a series of repeated measurements or is the agreement of a series of measurements concerning some quantity. Accuracy expresses the correctness of a measurement, whereas precision expresses the reproducibility of a measurement.

In this experiment, students will evaluate the precision and accuracy of various volume measuring devices. The statistical evaluations will include the *mean error*, ME, and *standard deviation*, s. The ME is a measure of accuracy, and is the average difference with regard to sign between the measured results and the "true" results, The ME is determined by

$$ME = \frac{\sum_{i=1}^{N}\left(X_i - \hat{X}_i\right)}{(N)} \qquad (1.4)$$

where X_i is the measured value, $\hat{X}_i$ is the true value, and N is the number of trials or replicates. As the accuracy of the method increases, ME will approach zero. A large "+" or "−" ME indicates the method produces values consistently higher or lower than the true value, respectively. A large deviation from zero indicates a *bias* or the presence of *determinate error*. Determinate errors are errors that are reproducible and can be discovered and corrected. Determinate errors can be: (1) operational and personal errors associated with the actions of the analyst not the method itself, e.g., incorrectly reading a buret, under or over washing precipitates in a gravimetric analysis, or the adsorption of water before massing, (2) instrumental or reagent errors such as failure to calibrate instrument, degradation of parts in the instrument, or improperly standardizing reagents, or (3) method errors, which occur as a consequence of the incompleteness of a reaction and/or incorrect sampling protocol. Operational and personal errors can be minimized or eliminated with proper training and experience, which is an objective of this experiment.

The standard deviation is a measure of precision of a method and is determined by

$$s = \sqrt{\frac{\sum_{i=1}^{N}[(x_i - \hat{x}_i) - ME]^2}{(N - 1)}} \tag{1.5}$$

The smaller the s the more precise the method. If s is smaller than ME, the method precision is greater than the accuracy, which is not uncommon. An experimental condition in which the ME is similar to or slightly $<s$ is ideal.

This laboratory experiment provides the beginning General Chemistry student experience in making common scientific measurements. Students develop a level of proficiency using balances and volumetric glassware, and are able to evaluate the inherent uncertainties associated with each type of measurement. By conducting the lab, students become better able to discern which labware is appropriate for the desired level of accuracy.

Student Learning Outcomes: Upon completion of this laboratory experiment, students will be able to:

1. Perform length, mass, and volume measurements and report the measurements with the correct degree of certainty.
2. Use mass and volume measurements to determine the density of a solid object.
3. Perform various calculations and report results with correct significant figures.
4. Make correct unit conversions using dimensional analysis.
5. Correctly deliver liquid using various graduated volume-delivering devices.

6. Perform mean error, ME, and standard deviation, s, calculations.

7. Evaluate the precision and accuracy of various graduated volume-delivering devices.

 SAFETY NOTE: *Even though this laboratory experiment requires the use of water only, students are expected to wear their goggles at all times. Glassware can, and often does, break during this experiment causing the potential for serious injury.*

MATERIALS AND METHODS

Materials: 50-mL Burets; plastic vials with caps; 100-mL graduated cylinders; Paper rulers with varying degrees of precision; No. 1 rubber stoppers; balances capable of measuring to the nearest 0.01 and 0.0001 g; thermometer; 25-mL volumetric pipets; 400–600 mL graduated beaker; 100-mL or 150-mL graduated beakers; distilled water.

Methods

The first thing the student should do is obtain approximately 400–500 mL of distilled water in a clean beaker, cover with a sheet of plastic wrap to keep dirt out, and allow the water to come to room temperature. This is your water supply for Part 3 of the experiment. Students should do Parts 1 and 2 while the water temperature equilibrates.

Part 1. Length Measurements

1. Use a pair of scissors and carefully cut out rulers A and B located on page 21 of this laboratory exercise. Measure the length and width (inside the border lines) of the rectangle printed below using rulers A and B. Note the smallest division on ruler A and B are 1 and 0.1 cm, so measured values should be estimated to the nearest 0.1 and 0.01 cm, respectively.

width

length

Part 2. Density Measurements

1. Using an electronic top-loading balance ($\pm$0.01 g), measure and record the mass of a dry 50-mL beaker (tare mass).
2. Place a no. 1 rubber stopper in the massed beaker, and record their combined mass (gross mass).
3. Fill a 100-mL graduated cylinder approximately halfway with distilled water.
4. Accurately read the water level in the cylinder and record the initial cylinder volume.
5. Tilt the graduated cylinder slightly and carefully let the massed stopper slide down the inside wall of the cylinder. Be careful to avoid splashing.
6. Tap the cylinder so the stopper sinks to the bottom. Swirl the water gently to remove air bubbles clinging to the stopper.
7. Accurately record the final cylinder volume.

Part 3. Accuracy and Precision of Volume Measurements

This part of the laboratory experience provides the student with a realistic evaluation of the accuracy and precision of common volume measurements made in the general chemistry laboratory. Note: Slight variations exist among balances, so BE SURE TO USE THE SAME BALANCE FOR EACH SUCCESSIVE MEASUREMENT. Methods for this experiment were adopted from references (1) and (2).

Part 3A. The Pipet

1. Obtain a plastic vial with cap and rinse thoroughly with distilled water. Dry the outside of the vial and cap with a Kimwipe or clean towel. The inside if the vial need not be dry.
2. Clean a 25-mL volumetric pipet with detergent (10% micro) and hot tap water; rinse with hot tap water and then with distilled water.
3. Mass the vial plus cap on the electronic analytical balance ($\pm$0.0001 g) and record as the *tare* mass. Be sure to "zero" the balance before use.
4. Pipet 25 mL of the temperature equilibrated water into the tared plastic vial. Put the cap on the vial and mass the vial plus cap plus 25 mL of water on the analytical balance and record as the *gross* mass. Subtract the tare mass from the gross mass to obtain the mass of water.
5. Discard the water in the vial and remass the empty vial plus cap. This is now your new tare mass.
6. Repeat steps 4 and 5 two more times for a total of three trials.
7. Record the temperature of your equilibrated water, and determine the density of water at the observed temperature to five significant figures using the data from the CRC handbook of Chemistry and Physics.

Part 3B. The Buret

1. Obtain a plastic vial with cap and rinse thoroughly with distilled water. Dry the outside of the vial and cap with a Kimwipe or clean towel. The inside of the vial need not be dry.

2. Using a buret brush, clean a 50-mL buret with detergent (10% micro) and hot tap water; rinse with hot tap water and then with distilled water.

3. Fill the buret well above the zero mark, and then expel air bubbles by simultaneously clicking the buret tip as you drain into a waste beaker. Drain buret until the bottom of meniscus is below the 0.00 mL. Touch off any hanging drop at the tip of the buret against the inside wall of the beaker. Note: the initial buret reading should be below the 0.00 mL level, i.e., the initial reading should be >0.00 mL. Do not attempt to place the meniscus at exactly 0.00 mL.

4. Mass the vial plus cap on the electronic analytical balance (± 0.0001 g) and record as the *tare* mass for trial 1. Be sure to "zero" the balance before use.

5. Record the initial buret reading to the proper level of significance. Drain approximately 20 mL of water into the tared plastic vial. Touch off any hanging drop at the tip of the buret against the inside wall of the vial. Allow the buret reading to stabilize for ca. 30 seconds before recording the final buret reading to the proper level of significance.

6. Put the cap on the vial and mass the vial plus cap plus 20 mL of water on the analytical balance and record as the *gross* mass for trial 1.

7. Discard the water in the vial and remass the empty vial plus cap. This is now your new tare mass for trial 2.

8. Drain a small amount of water from your buret to establish a new initial volume. This minimizes inherent correlation between successive volume deliveries and thus provides for a more effective statistical evaluation. Allow the buret reading to stabilize for ca. 30 seconds and then record the initial buret reading to the proper level of significance.

9. Again, drain approximately 20 mL of water into the newly tared plastic vial. Touch off any hanging drop at the tip of the buret against the inside wall of the vial. Allow the buret reading to stabilize for ca. 30 seconds before recording the final buret reading to the proper level of significance.

10. Put the cap on the vial and mass the vial plus cap plus 20 mL of water on the analytical balance and record as the *gross* mass for trial 2.

11. Discard the water in the vial and remass the empty vial plus cap. This is now your new tare mass for trial 3.

12. Refill the buret, and again drain to a level *below* the 0.00 mL. Allow the buret to stabilize, and then record the initial buret reading to the proper level of significance.

13. Drain approximately 20 mL of water into the tared plastic vial. Touch off any hanging drop at the tip of the buret against the inside wall of the vial. Allow the buret reading to stabilize for ca. 30 seconds before recording the final buret reading to the proper level of significance.

14. Put the cap on the vial and mass the vial plus cap plus 20 mL of water on the analytical balance and record as the *gross* mass for trial 3.

Part 3C. The Graduated Cylinder

1. Obtain a 100- or 150-mL graduated beaker to use as a "receiving" beaker.

2. Zero a top-loading balance and then mass the "receiving" beaker to the nearest 0.01 g. This is your beaker's tare mass, which is used in calculating the net water mass.

3. Add ca. 50 mL of the temperature-equilibrated water to your 100-mL graduated cylinder. Allow the water level to stabilize and then record the cylinder reading to the proper level of significance.

4. Completely transfer the water from the cylinder to the "receiving" beaker, and then mass the beaker plus water delivered. Record this gross mass, i.e., mass of "receiving" beaker plus water, in your notebook to the nearest 0.01 g.

5. Pour the water from the "receiving" beaker back into your source water container for reuse.

6. Repeat steps 2–5 two more times for a total of three trials. Make sure to use the same balance for all trials, and wipe off any excess water that might collect on the outside of the beaker prior to massing.

Part 3D. The Graduated Beaker

1. Obtain two 100- or 150-mL graduated beakers. Use one beaker as the "receiving" beaker, and the other as the "measuring" beaker.

2. Zero a top-loading balance and then mass the "receiving" beaker to the nearest 0.01 g. This is your beaker's tare mass, which is used in calculating the net water mass.

3. Fill the graduated "measuring" beaker with the temperature-equilibrated water until the beaker reads exactly 50 mL. Use a plastic transfer pipet to adjust the final volume. The BOTTOM of the meniscus should just touch the top of the calibration mark when looking STRAIGHT at it.

4. Completely transfer the 50 mL of water to the "receiving" beaker and then mass the "receiving" beaker plus 50 mL of water. Record this gross mass, i.e., mass of "receiving" beaker plus 50 mL of water, in your notebook to the nearest 0.01 g.

5. Pour the water from the "receiving" beaker back into your source water container for reuse.

6. Repeat steps 2–5 two more times for a total of three trials. Make sure to use the same balance for all trials, and wipe off any excess water that might collect on the outside of the beaker prior to massing.

Calculations

Part 1. Length Measurements

1. Calculate the Area [equation (1.1)], and Perimeter [equation (1.2)] of the rectangle below in cm units and report your results with the correct number of significant figures.

Part 2. Density Measurements

1. Determine the stopper mass by subtracting the tare mass from the gross mass.

2. Determine the stopper volume by subtracting the initial cylinder volume from the final volume.

3. Calculate stopper density by using equation (1.6). Record results in the correct number of significant figures.

$$\text{Density} = \left(\frac{\text{mass, g.}}{\text{Volume, mL}} \right) \tag{1.6}$$

Part 3A. The Pipet

1. For each trial, determine the net mass of water delivered from the pipet by subtracting the tare mass from the gross mass.

2. Calculate the true mass of water for each trial using the equation for buoyancy correction. That is, when calibrating with water, a buoyancy correction needs to be made because the built in mass on the balance are denser than the water being massed. The buoyancy correction is usually neglected when massing solids, but it is necessary for low-density materials like water. The following approximate equation should be used for calculating the true mass of water (M_{corr}):

$$M_{corr} = \left(\frac{M_{meas}}{0.9989} \right) \tag{1.7}$$

where M_{meas} is the measured mass of the water, i.e., the difference between the gross mass of water (plastic vial + cap + 25 mL of water) and the tare mass (plastic vial + cap).

3. Calculate the "true" volume for each M_{corr} delivered by the pipet using equation (1.8)

$$\text{True volume} = \hat{X}_i = \left(\frac{M_{corr}}{\rho_{water}} \right) \qquad (1.8)$$

where ρ_{water} is the density of water at the experimental temperature you recorded in Part 3A, step 7 of the Methods section.

4. Determine the mean error, ME, of this method using equation (1.4), where X_i is the measured or nominal value stamped on the pipet and = 25.00 mL, $\hat{X}_i$ is the true volume, and N is the number of trials, i.e., 3.

5. Determine the standard deviation using equation (1.5).

Part 3B. The Buret

1. For each trial, determine the net mass of water delivered from the buret by subtracting the tare mass from the gross mass.

2. Calculate the true mass, M_{corr}, of water for each trial using the equation for buoyancy correction, equation (1.7).

3. Calculate the "true" volume for each M_{corr} using equation (1.8).

4. Determine the mean error, ME, and standard deviation, s, of this method using equations (1.4) and (1.5), respectively. X_i = final buret reading minus the initial buret reading.

Part 3C. The Graduated Cylinder

1. For each trial, determine the net mass of water delivered from the cylinder by subtracting the beaker's tare mass from the gross mass (beaker + water).

2. Calculate the true mass, M_{corr}, of water for each trial using the equation for buoyancy correction, equation (1.7).

3. Calculate the "true" volume for each M_{corr} using equation (1.8).

4. Determine the mean error, ME, and standard deviation, s, of this method using equations (1.4) and (1.5), respectively. X_i is the cylinder reading prior to massing.

Part 3D. The Graduated Beaker

1. For each trial, determine the net mass of water delivered from the beaker by subtracting the beaker's tare mass from the gross mass (beaker + water).

2. Calculate the true mass, M_{corr}, of water for each trial using the equation for buoyancy correction, equation (1.7).

3. Calculate the "true" volume for each M_{corr} using equation (1.8).
4. Determine the mean error, ME, and standard deviation, s, of this method using equations (1.4) and (1.5), respectively. $X_i = 5 \times 10^1$ or 50 mL.

Results

In the "Results" section of your notebook, you should have table(s) summarizing your results. Tables 1.1 and 1.2 are examples of how your results tables could be constructed.

Discussion and Conclusions

As part of your discussion, write a short paragraph discussing your area and perimeter results, and how the level of certainty varied between the two rulers. Also, discuss your results related to the density of the rubber stopper. Which measurement dictated the level of significance in your result?

Consider the relative accuracies and precision of the pipet, buret, graduated cylinder, and graduated beaker. Which volume-measuring device is the most accurate/precise? Which volume-measuring device is the least accurate/precise? Is there evidence of determinate error in any of the volume-delivering methods, i.e., is your ME markedly greater than or less than zero. To what do you attribute these inaccuracies?

TABLE 1.1 Summary of results for the length and density measurements of parts A and B, respectively.

Determination	Ruler A	Ruler B
Area, cm²	_____	_____
Perimeter, cm	_____	_____
Density		
Stopper volume, mL	_____	
Stopper mass, g	_____	
Density, g mL⁻¹	_____	

TABLE 1.2 Summary of results for the volume measurements of part C.

Measurement Type	Trial 1	Trial 2	Trial 3	Stat. Result
25-mL Pipet				
Nominal vol., mL	25.00	25.00	25.00	------
Net mass, g	_____	_____	_____	------
True vol., mL	_____	_____	_____	------
ME				_____
Std. Dev., s				_____
Buret				
Measured vol., mL	_____	_____	_____	
Net mass, g	_____	_____	_____	------
True Vol., mL	_____	_____	_____	------
ME				------
Std. Dev., s				_____
				_____
Grad. Cylinder				
Measured vol., mL	_____	_____	_____	
Net mass, g	_____	_____	_____	------
True vol., mL	_____	_____	_____	------
ME				------
Std. Dev., s				_____
				_____
Grad. Beaker				
Beaker vol., mL	50	50	50	------
Net mass, g	_____	_____	_____	------
True vol., mL	_____	_____	_____	------
ME				_____
Std. Dev., s				_____

REFERENCES

The "bull's eye target" component of the opening collage image was excerpted from Flowers, P.; Theopold, K.; Langley, R.; Robinson, W. OpenStax College, *Chemistry*, OpenStax College. 2017. (https://openstax.org/details/books/chemistry).

1. Brown, T. L.; Lemay, E. H., Jr.; Bursten, B. E.; Murphy, C. J.; Woodard, P. M.; M. W. Stoltzfus. *Chemistry: The Central Science*, 13th ed.; Pearson Education, Inc.: New Jersey, 2015.

2. Rice, J. *Analytical Chemistry I: An introduction to Quantitative Analysis*. Laboratory Manual, South Dakota State University: Brookings, SD, 1995.

RULER A

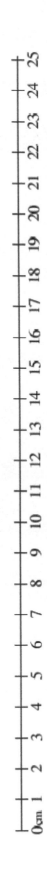

RULER B

Introduction to Gas Chromatography and Mass Spectrometry (GC-MS)

INTRODUCTION

Theory: Careers in the chemical and biological sciences increasingly necessitate graduates with scientific skills that foster an interrelational approach to long-term ecological health. The need for graduates with interdisciplinary **prowess** and that are adept in acquiring, interpreting, and communicating scientific information is on the rise. Students that graduate from higher educational institutions in the Science, Technology, Engineering, and Math (STEM) disciplines must be able to assume a problem-solving approach to acquiring knowledge.

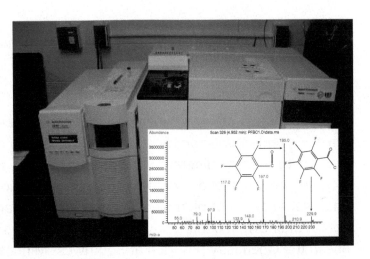

Source: Frank Schindler

The very foundation to scientific inquiry is formulating an atomic interpretation or mental picture of the possible ways molecules interact, and thus describe laboratory observations with chemical formulas and structures. Instrumentation technology facilitates this process and enhances the scientist's ability to study matter and provide a molecular interpretation of the visible world. Chemical instrumentation technology, however, is continually changing. Instruments are being designed with greater sensitivity and lower detection limits, all in effort to enhance the scientist's ability to qualify and quantify unknown compounds in mixtures. Many companies that hire technicians, for example,

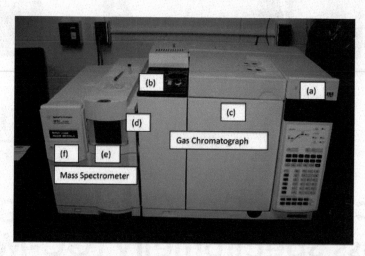

FIGURE 2.1   The Agilent 7890A Gas chromatograph (GC) and 5975C Mass spectrometer (MS) used at Southwest Minnesota State University. Image shows (a) local control panel for GC, (b) sample injection port, (c) GC oven containing GC column, (d) Mass Selective Detector (MSD) interface, (e) MSD, and (f) MSD local control panel. *Source: Frank Schindler*

expect individuals to master laboratory instrumentation and procedures, and be able to think critically, solve problems, and communicate information effectively through writing and verbal presentation.

Two of the most common analytical techniques used in chemistry are *gas chromatography* (GC) and *mass spectrometry* (MS). GC-MS is a coupling of the two techniques and is used to identify different substances within a test sample. Applications of GC-MS include drug detection, detection of power residues from explosives, environmental analysis, analysis of biomolecules and proteins, and/or the identification and quantitation of unknown mixture components. Figure 2.1 shows the GC-MS system currently in use in the Chemistry program at Southwest Minnesota State University (SMSU).

Gas chromatography (GC) is a common technique used in analytical chemistry that permits separation, identification, and determination of components of gaseous mixtures via a mobile and immobile (stationary) phase separation. In GC, the mobile phase is an inert carrier gas such as He, H_2 or N_2. The stationary phase is a thin (i.e., 0.25 μm) film of a polymeric material inside a piece of glass or stainless steel tubing some 30 m in length called a column (Fig. 2.2).[1] The polymer material used in the GC column of the SMSU's Chemistry Program is 5% diphenyl 95% dimethyl polysiloxane. The separation of mixture components takes place because each gaseous species has a different affinity for the stationary phase. This variable affinity governs the rate at which a particular component elutes from the column, i.e., its retention time.

Specifically with GC, a mixture of compounds to be analyzed is injected into the GC sample injection port using a micro syringe [Fig. 2.1 (b)] where the mixture is vaporized

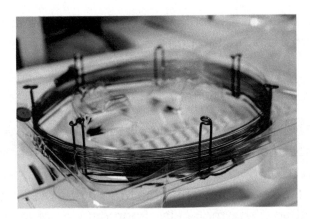

FIGURE 2.2 Typical GC column. Image extracted from Agilent MSD operation manual.[1]
Source: Frank Schindler

in a heated chamber. The gas mixture travels through a GC column located in the GC oven compartment [Fig. 2.1 (c)], where the compounds become separated as they interact with the column. As the compounds separate, they elute from the column and enter a detector. The detector is capable of creating an electronic signal whenever the presence of a compound is detected. The chromatogram in Fig. 2.3 is an example showing the peak that results from GC separation of pentafluorobenzoyl chloride (PFBC). The size of the signal or height of peak corresponds to the quantity of compound present in the sample. As the individual compounds elute from the GC column, they immediately enter the mass spectrometer through the mass selective detector (MSD) interface [Fig. 2.1 (d)].

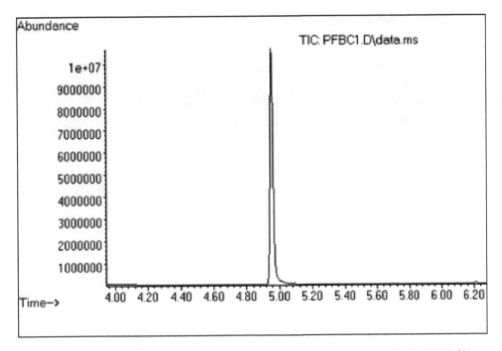

FIGURE 2.3   Total ion current (TIC) chromatogram of pentafluorobenzoyl chloride (PFBC).
Source: Frank Schindler

Mass spectrometry is an analytical tool used to determine the atomic mass of the components separated from a mixture through electron bombardment and ionization according to equation (2.1).[2]

$$M + e^- \rightarrow M^+ + 2\,e^- \qquad (2.1)$$

The M in equation (2.1) is the unionized molecular fragment and M^+ is the ionized molecular fragment. The most common method of ionization is *electron impact* (EI). In EI, accelerated electrons are produced from a heated tungsten filament. The electrons bombard the separated molecules as they enter the MSD at the MSD interface causing immediate molecular ionization.[2] The molecular fragments or charged ions are separated according to their mass-to-charge ratio (m/z or m/e) by advancement through a magnetic field. The magnetic field deflects each ion differently, the extent of deflection being a function of their mass. Figure 2.4 is an image extracted from Flowers et al. (2017) showing an example of gaseous atoms introduced into a MSD.[3]

Figure 2.5 shows the mass spectrum for pentafluorobenzoyl chloride (PFBC). Assuming the ion fragments formed from electron bombardment are singly charged, then the m/z represented by the x-axis in Fig. 2.5 represents the fragment mass. The fragment furthest to the right (molecular peak) is the heaviest and generally represents the molecular

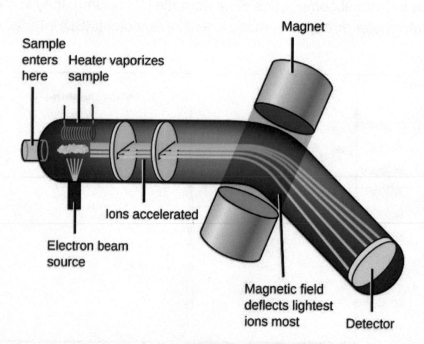

FIGURE 2.4 A mass spectrometer. Sample atoms are introduced at the mass detector interface as they come off the gas chromatograph column. The atoms are ionized to form M^+ ions, which are then directed through a magnetic field. The paths of the ions of the two Cl isotopes diverge as they pass through the field.[3] *Download for free at https://openstax.org/details/books/chemistry*

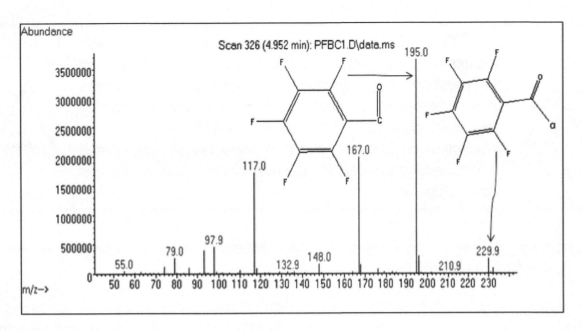

FIGURE 2.5 Mass spectrum of pentafluorobenzoyl chloride (PFBC). PFBC is shown at $m/z = 230$.
Source: Frank Schindler

mass, while the highest or most intense peak in the mass spectrum is called the base peak and is used to set 100% relative abundance. That is, the relative abundance of each peak in Fig. 2.5 may be expressed as a percentage of the base peak.

The mass spectrum serves as a "fingerprint" for the molecule, and is used to identify the compound. That is, known spectra in a library database are compared to the mass spectrum from a sample component, and then a report of likely identifications along with the statistical probability of the match is generated.

This experiment follows the concept and procedures discussed in Pfennig and Schaefer (2011).[4] Students are introduced to the use of the GC-MS instrumentation and to the interpretation of spectra generated from the GC-MS method.

Student Learning Outcomes: Upon completion of this laboratory experiment, students will be able to:

1. Use the GC to acquire a total ion chromatogram and then calculate the mass percent of dichloromethane and acetone in an unknown mixture.
2. Evaluate the peaks in the mass spectrum of a halogenated compound to determine the isotopic composition and the atomic mass of chlorine.

The experimental procedures for this experiment were adapted from the publication of Pfennig and Schaefer (2011).[4]

SAFETY NOTE: *Dichloromethane and toluene are eye and skin irritants and are potential carcinogens. Extreme caution should be exercised when handling these chemicals. Excess samples should be properly disposed of in the appropriately labeled recovered chemical bottle located in the fume hood. Also, students need to be careful when using the GC syringe and when injecting sample into the hot injection port on the gas chromatograph.[4]*

MATERIALS AND METHODS

Materials: Agilent 7890A GC System with 5975C MSD detector; standard solutions of HPLC-grade acetone and dichloromethane (50.0 μL of each analyte brought to a final volume of 50 mL with reagent-grade toluene); an unknown mixture of HPLC-grade acetone and dichloromethane in toluene; 10 μL GC micro-pipet.

Methods

Part 1. Sample Preparation

1. Make up known standard solutions by micropipeting 100 μL each of pure reagent, HPLC-grade CH_2Cl_2 (dichloromethane) and C_3H_6O (acetone or propanone) into two separate 100 mL volumetric flasks. Bring the flask to volume with toluene. Cap the flask, wrap with Parafilm, and mix several times by inversion. Solutions must be capped and wrapped in Parafilm to minimize evaporative loss. Solutions must remain capped until immediately preceding injection into the GC-MS. This is a 0.1% (v/v) solution.

2. The instructor will provide an unknown solution of dichloromethane and acetone for analysis.

Part 2. Sample Injection and Spectra Acquisition

1. Go to the GC-MS room (ST 214A) and load the GC/MSD ChemStation® software by double clicking the GCMS shortcut icon on the PC desktop. The **Instrument Control** window is displayed when you load the software. This is where you set and monitor instrument parameters. The Instrument Control view is shown in Fig. 2.6.

2. Click on the load method icon 🔳 in the "Method" section. Select the method "Intro_GCMS.m" located in the C:\msdchem\1\methods\Gen_Chem\ folder. This "Method" contains all the GC-MS acquisition parameters needed to run your sample, and has been created for you.

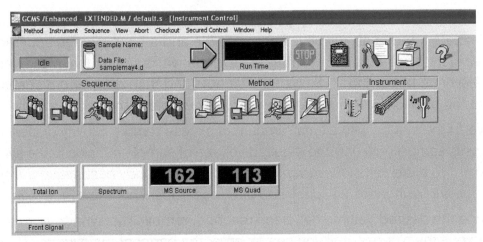

FIGURE 2.6   The Instrument Control view in GC/MSD ChemStation®.[5] *Source: Frank Schindler*

© Agilent Technologies, Inc. 2005. Reproduced with Permission, Courtesy of Agilent Technologies, Inc.

Note: the MSD has been tuned with the same GC oven temperature, column flow, and analyzer temperatures that will be used for data acquisition.

3. Prepare the GC syringe by doing the following:

WARNING: SYRINGE IS VERY FRAGILE. BE EXTREMELY CAREFUL WHEN EXTRACTING SOLUTIONS!

a. **Clean** the syringe by drawing acetone into the syringe and injecting the acetone onto a Kimwipe or paper towel. Do this several times. Repeat cleaning procedure with a solvent toluene.

b. **Condition** the 10 μL GC syringe with the sample to be injected by inserting the needle of the syringe below the surface of the sample and drawing the sample into the syringe. Discard the rinsate in an appropriate container. Repeat this procedure several times.

c. Wipe the needle of the syringe with a Kimwipe, and place it down on a clean towel or Kimwipe until you are ready to fill the syringe.

4. Click on the GC Parameters ⬚ icon in the "Instrument" section. Select "Detectors" and then "FID Front." Check, √ , the "Heater," "H_2 Flow," "Air Flow," "Makeup Flow (He)," and "Flame" checkboxes. Click "OK."

5. Click on the Run Method icon ⬚ in the "Method" section.

6. When the **Start Run** dialog box appears, specify the following sample information: (1) **Operator Name**; (2) a unique **Data Path** for the sample, i.e., C:\msdchem\1\data\Gen_Chem\; (3) a unique **Data File Name** for the sample, e.g., Known_1.d; and (4) **Misc Info** (optional) to document the injection.

7. Make sure that the **Data Acquisition** option is selected.

8. Ready the GC syringe for sample injection by doing the following:

    a. Eliminate trapped air, which is compressible and affects syringe accuracy and precision, by completely **priming** the syringe with sample. Insert the needle of the syringe below the surface of the sample and then draw and dispense sample into the solution until bubbles are no longer visible in the syringe barrel.

    b. Overfill the syringe with a small amount of excess sample. Slowly dispense the excess sample until only the required volume of sample remains in the syringe, i.e., 1.0 µL. *To avoid variations in sample volume due to body heat, grasp the syringe flange and plunger as you draw and dispense fluids. This helps reduce inaccuracy.*

    c. Once the desired volume has been reached, remove the syringe from the sample and pull the plunger until you see air enter the barrel of the syringe. There should now be a plug of air before and after the sample within the syringe. Wipe the needle clean with a Kimwipe, and avoid wicking sample with the tissue by making sure it does not come in contact with the needle opening. The syringe is now ready for injection.

Note: The processes of cleaning with acetone and solvent, and then conditioning and priming syringe should always be done between samples to prevent sample carryover or contamination.

9. Click **Run Method** to initiate the run. If the GC temperatures are not stable, the message "**Waiting for GC ready. . .**" is displayed.

10. When the GC is stable and ready for injection, the message "**Waiting for remote start. . .To manual override, click Start Run**" will appear.

11. Once the instrument is ready for injection, inject the sample into the GC at the injection port [Fig. 2.1 (b)] by inserting the syringe needle through the septum of the port. You will feel some resistance. Depress the plunger to inject the sample and then immediately initiate the run by clicking on "**Start Run**". *Injection technique is important since the shape and width of the peak is dependent upon its reproducibility.*

12. Once the run has started, a window appears that says, "**Override solvent delay [X minutes]?**" **Always** either ignore **this message (it will go away at the end of the pre-set solvent delay) or select NO!!!** Note: The method run time, i.e., acquisition time is 4 minutes. The total time is 6 minutes, due to a 2-min post run where the oven temperature is held at 150°C to bake off the toluene solvent in preparation for the next sample injection.[4]

13. While the acquisition is in progress, ready the syringe for the next sample, i.e., the unknown sample, by cleaning and conditioning (Steps 3a–3c), and readying for injection (Steps 8a–8c).

14. Perform an acquisition of the unknown sample by performing Steps 9–11.

15. When acquisitions of both samples are complete, clean the syringe for the next group as outlined in Step 2a. Remove the plunger, but DO NOT touch it, and wipe

clean with a Kimwipe. Reinsert the plunger into the syringe barrel. BE EXTREMELY CAREFUL WHEN REINSERTING PLUNGER! IT BENDS EASILY!

Part 3. Data Analysis

1. Minimize the **Instrument Control** window and then load the data analysis software by double clicking the GCMS shortcut icon on the PC desktop.

2. Load the appropriate data file by clicking on Load Data File. . .in the File menu. Change path if needed to C:\msdchem\1\data\Gen_Chem_data and then select your data file for the acetone standard. Select OK. You should have a data analysis window [2] TIC: filename.D\data.ms.

3. You may have to scale your chromatogram. Your instructor will help you.

4. Enlarge the window by mouse dragging and then select Copy Window. . . from the Tools menu. Input window # to copy to clipboard. Select OK.

5. Go to Start and load WordPad®. Paste the image as a picture[metafile]. Minimize the window.

6. In the data analysis window, record the retention time of the primary acetone peak. Integrate the peak to obtain the area under the curve. The instructor will help you do this.

7. Select "Integration Results" from the Chromatogram menu. Record the area of the primary peak in your notebook. You will use this value to calculate the instrument response factor.

8. Perform steps 2–7 for your dichloromethane sample, and again for your unknown mixture.

9. Again, load your dichloromethane data file. Double click the right mouse button on the time point of interest in the chromatogram, i.e., the peak's retention time. The mass spectrum appears in window [1].

10. Enlarge the mass spectrum window by mouse dragging and then select Copy Window. . . from the Tools menu. Input window #1 to copy to clipboard. Select OK.

11. Go to WordPad®. Paste the image as a picture[metafile]. You should now have four graphs in WordPad®, i.e., your chromatograms of standard acetone, standard dichloromethane, unknown mixture, and the mass spectrum of the dichloromethane. Print two copies of these graphs. If using PLN, cut them out and tape one copy to your original notebook pages and one copy to your carbon copies of the notebook. If using ELN, save the image and then insert it into your ELN.

12. Go back to your dichloromethane mass spectrum and select "Tabulate" from the Spectrum menu, and record the exact *m/z* and the associated abundances for each molecular fragment at *m/z* 49, 51, 84, 86, and 88.

13. Assign the molecular fragments associated with *m/z* 49 and 51, and draw the molecular ion formulas on your mass spectrum. Figure 2.7 shows an example of this assignment for nominal masses 86 and 88 of dichloromethane.

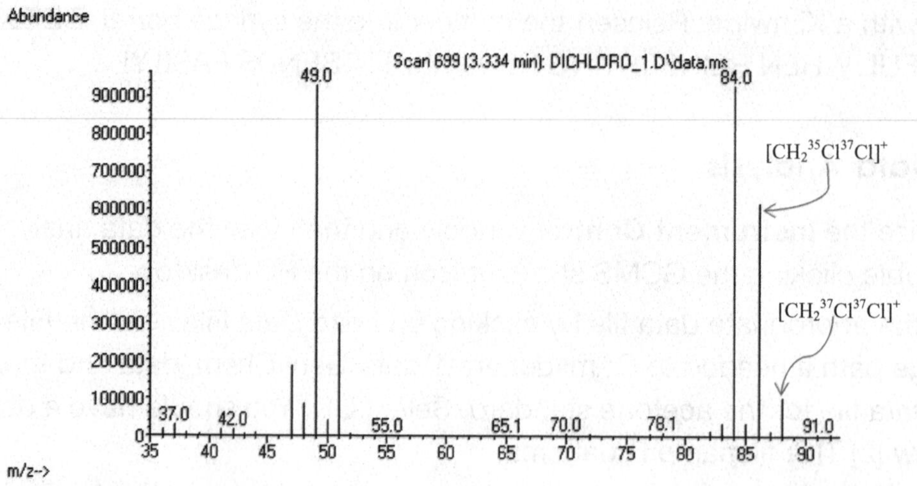

FIGURE 2.7   Mass spectrum of dichloromethane showing molecular ion fragment assignment for masses 86 and 88. *Source: Frank Schindler*

14. Compare your standard analyte chromatograms with the chromatogram of your unknown mixture. Identify the component peaks of the analytes in the unknown solution based on the one-to-one correlation with the retention times of the pure substances. Are dichloromethane and acetone present in your unknown mixture?

Calculations

1. Using the Single-Point External Standard method for your standard acetone and dichloromethane samples, calculate the instrument **Response Factor** (*RF*) using equation (2.2),

$$\text{Response Factor}_{Analyte} = RF_{Analyte} = \frac{\text{peak area}_{Analyte}}{\text{Sample volume, mL}} \tag{2.2}$$

where the analyte in this laboratory experiment is dichloromethane or acetone, and the sample volume is 0.001 mL. A *RF* needs to be calculated for each analyte of interest. The *RF* is unique to each instrument and analyte, and is needed to quantify the analyte in the unknown mixture.

2. Once the *RF* has been determined for each standard analyte, determine the analyte quantity in your unknown mixture, i.e., the analyte volume in this case, since the RF is based on injection volume.

$$\text{Analyte Quantity} = \frac{\text{peak area}_{Analyte}}{RF_{Analyte}} \tag{2.3}$$

The result of equation (2.3) is analyte volume. Look up the density of acetone and dichloromethane in the CRC handbook,[6] and determine the mass of each analyte using these values, i.e., multiply the analyte volume by the analyte density. From the respective grams of each analyte in the mixture, determine the mass percent of dichloromethane and acetone in the unknown mixture. Your result should be reported as percent acetone (m/m) and percent dichloromethane (m/m).

3. Given the actual concentration of analytes in the unknown mixture, calculate the relative percent error using equation (2.4)

$$\%\text{Relative error} = \frac{\text{measured mass percent} - \text{actual mass percent}}{\text{actual mass percent}} \times 100 \quad (2.4)$$

4. From the grouping of mass spectral peaks corresponding to m/z 49 and 51, and knowing that m/z 49 is considered the base peak in this grouping, and is thus assigned a relative abundance = 100, perform the following:

a. Calculate the relative abundance (%) of the two Cl isotopes by first setting the base peak equal to 100 and determining the percentage of the lesser peak. This is done by dividing the absolute abundance of the lesser peak by the absolute abundance of base peak. Find the total relative abundance by summing 100 (the base peak) and the percentage of lesser peak. To determine the relative abundance of the two Cl isotopes in turn, determine the quotient of the isotopic peak of interest over the total relative abundance.

b. Calculate the average atomic mass of chlorine by multiplying the relative abundance of each isotope by its atomic mass and summing the products. In determining the amu for each chlorine isotope, we assume the isotopic composition of C is essentially 100% ^{12}C with an atomic mass = 12.000 amu, and that of hydrogen is primarily ^{1}H with an atomic mass = 1.008 amu. For example, if the exact fragment mass for $[CH_2{}^{37}Cl{}^{37}Cl]^+$ is 88.00 (Fig. 2.7), then each ^{37}Cl isotope would have an atomic mass = 36.992 amu.

Results

In the "Results" section of your notebook, you should have table(s) summarizing your results related to both the ion chromatography and mass spectrometry methodology. The results should include response factors, mass percentages of acetone and dichloromethane, and percent errors as determined from the gas chromatograms, and the relative percentages of chlorine isotopes, atomic mass of each isotope, and the average atomic mass of chlorine as determined from the mass spectrum. Your results should also include the chromatograms for your standard analytes and the unknown mixture, and the mass spectrum of dichloromethane including the assigned molecular fragments at m/z 49 and 51.

Discussion/Conclusion

As part of your discussion, write a short paragraph discussing your results and the associated error. Conclude your mass percentages and average atomic mass of chlorine, and relate your results to the original experimental objectives: (1) Use the GC to acquire a total ion chromatogram and then calculate the mass percent of dichloromethane and acetone in an unknown mixture, and (2) Evaluate the peaks in the mass spectrum of a halogenated compound to determine the isotopic composition and the atomic mass of chlorine. Also, indicate how your calculated average atomic mass of chlorine compares to that listed on most periodic tables.

REFERENCES

1. Agilent Technologies, Inc. *Agilent 5975 Series MSD Operation Manual*. 3rd ed.; Agilent Technologies, Inc., 2010.

2. Brisdon, A. K. Mass Spectrometry. In *Inorganic Spectroscopic Methods*; Oxford University Press: New York, 2004; pp. 74–83.

3. Flowers, P.; Theopold, K.; Langley, R.; Robinson, W. *Chemistry*, OpenStax College. 2019. (https://openstax.org/details/books/chemistry-2e).

4. Pfennig, B. W.; Schaefer, A. K. The Use of Gas Chromatography and Mass Spectrometry To Introduce General Chemistry Students to Percent Mass and Atomic Mass Calculations *J. Chem. Educ.* **2011**, 88, 970–974.

5. Agilent Technologies, Inc. *Agilent G1701EA GC/MSD ChemStation: Getting Started.* Agilent Technologies, Inc. 2011.

6. *CRC Handbook of Chemistry and Physics*, 81st ed.; Lide, D. R., Ed.; CRC Press: Boca Raton, FL, 2000; Section 3, No. 206–207.

EXPERIMENT 3

Chemistry of Household Products

INTRODUCTION

A very important chemical property of any substance, but particularly solids, is that of water solubility. A substance that dissolves in water mixes completely to form a completely homogenous liquid mixture, called a solution. It is important to distinguish between a solution and a so-called solid suspension, which may appear homogeneous but actually consists of very fine solid particles. A solution is clear and, unless it has a color, appears indistinguishable from pure water. In a solid suspension, the solid particles give the liquid a cloudy appearance.

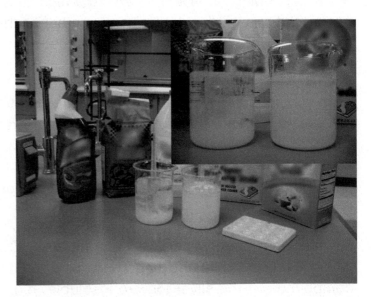

Source: Frank Schindler

Another important chemical property is the ionic or nonionic nature of a substance. Some substances are composed of positive (cations) and negative (anion) ions and others of neutral molecules. Some are more difficult to classify in that although they may be nonionic, they form ions in water solution. Hydrochloric acid, HCl(aq) is an example of a polar covalent, nonionic molecule that readily forms ions when added to water.

When the ions from one reactant seem to exchange with the ions of another reactant, a *double replacement* or *metathesis* reaction takes place with the subsequent formation of a sparingly soluble solid or *precipitate*. This is also known as a precipitation reaction. Formation of a precipitate may require a more detailed description of its physical character, for example, does the precipitation appear as a uniform cloudiness throughout (*finely divided*), does it appear as "fluffy," cottony tuffs (*flocculative* precipitate) or does it appear as a syrupy, gel-like substance (*gelatinous* precipitate). The color of the precipitate should also be included in your description, e.g., "a white gelatinous precipitate formed."

A very important feature of water solutions is that called "acidity"—and its opposite, "alkalinity" or "basicity." Substances classified as acids form positively charged hydrogen ions (H^+) when mixed with water and those classified as bases form negatively charged hydroxide ions (OH^-). Acids and bases may be classified strong or weak depending upon the extent to which they form these ions. Also, acidic and basic solutions will "neutralize" one another as these two ions combine to form water molecules. Note that a substance need not necessarily itself be ionic to be acidic or basic in water.

In this experiment, you will be observing reactions of several household products with some common laboratory reagents. The reagents used in this laboratory are: silver nitrate ($AgNO_3$; 0.1 M solution), thymol blue indicator (0.1% solution), hydrochloric acid (HCl; 6 M solution), and calcium chloride ($CaCl_2$; 1 M solution). The following paragraphs provide more detailed descriptions of each reagent:

Silver nitrate: A 0.1 M solution of silver nitrate ($AgNO_3$(aq)) is provided. Silver nitrate in water consists of silver (Ag^+) and nitrate (NO_3^-) ions. Positively charged ions are called *cations*, while the negatively charged ions are called *anions*. Many ionic compounds of the silver ion are insoluble, e.g., silver carbonate ($AgCO_3$). When a solution containing a solid-forming anionic species is mixed with silver nitrate, a precipitate forms. A precipitate is a solid formed from a reaction in solution. A reaction of this type is referred to as a *metathesis reaction*, which is covered in more detail in the "Investigating Copper Reactions" experiment. The $AgNO_3$ test is a common test for the presence of chloride (Cl^-) ion, which forms a silver chloride) precipitate (AgCl(s)) when silver nitrate is added. Many negative ions also form precipitates with silver ion.

Calcium chloride: This solution is also a solution of an ionic compound containing calcium (Ca^{2+}) and chloride (Cl^-). Just like silver nitrate solutions, it can form precipitates if mixed with something that causes an insoluble substance to form. This would most often occur with the calcium ion as most ionic compounds of chloride are soluble. The two most common precipitates seen with calcium ion are with the hydroxide (OH^-) ion and with the carbonate (CO_3^{2-}) ion. Calcium hydroxide is slightly soluble; therefore, a precipitate may or may not be seen when calcium is mixed with a basic solution. It depends upon how basic it is. Calcium carbonate is very insoluble. A very distinct precipitate can be seen whenever solutions containing the calcium ion and the carbonate ion are mixed.

Thymol blue indicator: There are a number of substances which change color depending upon how acidic or basic a solution is. Thymol blue is one of these. This particular indicator is red if the solution is very acidic. If the solution is only moderately acidic or neutral, it is yellow. Finally, thymol blue will turn blue in the presence of a solution that is moderately or strongly basic.

Hydrochloric acid: This is the most common laboratory acid. It is a strong acid and, as such, has a significant concentration of hydronium (H_3O^+) ions (or hydrogen ions, H^+). Two common reactions are worth mentioning. First, as a strong acid, it will neutralize bases. It ordinarily does so with the generation of a significant amount of heat. Second, it will react with substances containing the carbonate ion (CO_3^{2-}) or the hydrogen carbonate ion (HCO_3^-). Hydrogen carbonate ion is also called bicarbonate. The reaction produces carbon dioxide gas, evidenced by vigorous fizzing or effervescence.

The purpose of the experiment is to learn some common tests used in the laboratory and to use these tests to identify the important chemical properties of select household products. Chemicals, regardless of their origin or source, often react with other chemicals in a very characteristic way. Chemists look for these reaction characteristics or patterns and use them to deduce, predict, or identify unknown reactive species. This experiment is an example of a *qualitative* or observational experiment where you make observations related to the presence or the formation of some chemical species without trying to *quantify* or determine how much of it there is. As such, all of your observations should be recorded in the "Data" section of your notebook.

Student Learning Outcomes: Upon completion of this laboratory experiment, students will be able to:

1. Observe reaction patterns of several household products using select laboratory reagents.
2. Use the developed reaction patterns from known chemicals to deduce the reaction pattern and identify an unknown.
3. Research the active ingredients of select household products, and with current chemistry knowledge, relate laboratory observations to certain chemical properties of the select household products and an unknown solution.

SAFETY NOTE: *This laboratory experiment uses <u>concentrated acids</u> that are very corrosive causing severe skin and eye burns. <u>WEAR EYE PROTECTION AT ALL TIMES</u>. Any chemicals spilled on skin should be washed immediately with tap water. Neutralize acid or base sills with sodium bicarbonate, and sponge them up immediately. Empty your reaction plate wells into a large beaker, <u>with the exception of the silver nitrate, which should be emptied in the recovered chemical container located in the fume hood</u>, and then neutralize the contents of the beaker with ca. 2 g of sodium bicarbonate, adding enough water to dissolve the bicarbonate. Flush the neutralized solution down the drain with plenty of water. Collect all unused household products and reagents in a large beaker and perform the same disposal as outlined above for the reaction plate wells. The unused <u>silver nitrate</u> should be collected in the recovered chemical container located in the fume hood.*

MATERIALS AND METHODS

Materials: *Products:* Baking soda (a solid); Washing soda (a solid); Ordinary sugar (a solid); Household ammonia (a liquid solution); Lysol toilet bowl cleaner (a liquid solution); (Your instructor may choose others or make substitutions.), *Reagents:* Silver nitrate ($AgNO_3$; 0.1 M solution); Thymol blue indicator (0.1% solution); Hydrochloric acid (HCl; 6 M solution); Calcium chloride ($CaCl_2$; 1 M solution); A 5% solution of an unknown household chemical; plastic wrap for covering test tubes; polyethylene transfer pipets. Except for the distilled water, you will find the test reagents in convenient dropper bottles in the laboratory.

Methods

All observations related to this experiment should be recorded in the "Data and Observation" section of your notebook. Record the household chemicals and their active ingredient(s), and the chemical reagents in your notebook. Be certain to include brand names where appropriate. Given the qualitative nature of this laboratory experiment, there are no calculations; therefore, there is no need for a "Calculations" section in your notebook.

Part 1. Water Solubility

1. Secure three small test tubes. In the bottom of each one, place a small amount of one of the three solid household products. The solid should just barely fill the rounded bottom of the tube, but the exact amount is not critical.

2. Label the tubes and add distilled water so that each is about half full.

3. Cover each tube with a small piece of plastic wrap and shake vigorously for about a minute. In the "Data" section of your notebook, record what you observe. Draw a conclusion about the water solubility of each solid. Note: Often a water-soluble solid might take some time to completely dissolve. Thus, a considerable amount of suspended solid might remain after a minute of shaking even if the solid is soluble. If you see the amount of visible solid decreasing as you shake, you can conclude that the substance is soluble even if some cloudiness remains.

4. If you conclude any of these solids are water soluble, save the test tube with the liquid solution for Part 2.

Part 2. Testing Solutions with the Laboratory Reagents

1. You have up to three solutions of household products in labeled test tubes from Part 1. Obtain small samples of the two other products (liquid ammonia cleaner and Lysol toilet bowl cleaner) in two additional test tubes. Add some distilled water to each tube so that each is about one-half to two-thirds full. Each of these five solutions is to be tested with each of the four chemical reagents listed above.

2. Use a well plate (or plates) to carry out the tests. For the sake of keeping track of the many combinations, it may be convenient to arrange the combinations in a grid format on the well plates with each column corresponding to one of the chemical reagents and each row to one of the household products.

3. Using a polyethylene transfer pipet, place a few drops of the solution to be tested, i.e., the household chemical, into the appropriate reaction well followed by a few drops of the testing reagent. Observe what happens and write down your observations in your notebook with as much detail as possible. Particularly record any colors observed, visible reactions such as fizzing, heat evolution or absorption of heat, or the appearance, either quickly or with time, of a precipitate. It is also possible that a particular combination produces no reaction. If so, indicate this as well. If you have doubts about any particular combination, repeat that test in a test tube in order to better observe the results.

Part 3. Testing an Unknown Solution with the Laboratory Reagents

1. Clean a reaction plate, and then secure a small sample of the unknown in a clean test tube. Using a polyethylene transfer pipet, place a few drops of the unknown solution into four separate reaction wells, and then add a few drops of each test reagent into the appropriate well. Record all observations.

2. Compare the reaction patterns of the unknown with those established with the known household chemicals.

3. Deduce the reaction pattern of the unknown, and based on these patterns, identify the active ingredient in the unknown solution.

Results

Since this is an observational laboratory and all observations are recorded in the "Data and Observation" section of your notebook, there is no need for a "Results" section.

Discussion/Conclusion

In your data section of your notebook, you should have an accounting of observations detailing the unique, chemical patterns of the laboratory reagents and household chemicals. Many household products contain one primary active ingredient, i.e., the species that participates in the chemical reaction, but they may contain more. Obtain the active ingredient of the household products by either referring to the label on the container or by accessing the Consumer Product Information Database (CPID) at https://www. whatsinproducts.com. In addition, use the solubility guidelines of common ionic compounds in water located in your General Chemistry textbook to facilitate your discussion. Based on your observations, and the active ingredients of the household products, discuss the solubility of the household products and their reaction patterns. Are there household products that produce the same reactive observation with laboratory reagent? Would you be able to differentiate between two household products by using the same laboratory reagent? Are the experimental observations, including solubility and pH, related to the presence of a particular active ingredient(s)? Cation or anion?

Conclude the experiment with a statement relating the presence of the active ingredient (reactive species) with laboratory reagent. Based on your reactive pattern evaluation of the known reactive species, identify the active ingredient in the unknown solution.

Molar Mass of an Alkali Metal Hydroxide by Titration

INTRODUCTION

Group I and heavier Group II metals readily react with water forming hydrogen gas and a strong hydroxide. An example of this type of reaction can be seen with sodium metal

$$Na(s) + H_2O \rightarrow NaOH(aq) + \frac{1}{2}H_2(g) \tag{4.1}$$

where the sodium metal becomes oxidized (sodium metal loses an electron and is the reducing agent), and the H^+ of water becomes reduced (H^+ gains an electron and is the oxidizing agent) forming $H_2(g)$ and NaOH. The reaction of sodium with water is referred to as an oxidation-reduction and single replacement reaction. It's a single replacement reaction because the single element, sodium, replaces a H^+ in water by transferring its one valance electron to water.

Because NaOH is a strong electrolyte, it does not exist in aqueous solution as a discrete unit, but rather is completely ionized and exists as its respective ions, Na^+ and OH^-. We can readily determine the amount of OH^- produced from a given amount of metal using a procedure called an acid-base titration. In an acid-base titration, an acid of known concentration is delivered from a buret to a reaction flask containing the OH^-. The acid addition is continued until the moles of acid (H^+) added equal the amount of base (OH^-) present in the reaction flask. This is called the *equivalence*

Source: Frank Schindler

41

point and is estimated using a color-changing indicator, which is called the *end-point* of titration. The end-point of a titration is an observable, physical change and provides an estimation of the *equivalence point* of titration. The equivalence point is the point of titration where stoichiometrically equivalent quantities of acid and base have reacted. Figure 4.1 illustrates the titration process and explains the typical progression of a titration.

FIGURE 4.1 Procedure for titrating an acid against a standard solution of base. A known aliquot volume (or mass if acid is in its solid form and has not been dissolved in water, e.g., KHP) of unknown acid is quantitatively added to an Erlenmeyer flask (A); an appropriate pH indicator is added to the flask and mixed (B); a buret is conditioned with the standard base solution, filled to above the zero mark, drained to eliminate air bubbles, and then initial buret reading taken after one to two minutes of meniscus stabilization (C); unknown acid titrated until a faint pink appears and stays for 13–15 seconds. Note the color of the end-point depends on indicator used. In this image, phenolphthalein is used, so the end-point of titration is light pink. If the solution becomes dark pink to red, you have gone well beyond the equivalence point and the titration must be repeated with a new sample aliquot. *Source: Frank Schindler*

Adding an acid such as hydrochloric acid, HCl, to the base NaOH is called a neutralization reaction, and can be represented as

$$NaOH(aq) + HCl(aq) \rightarrow NaCl(aq) + H_2O(l) \tag{4.2}$$

If we write equation (4.2) in its net ionic form we would have

$$OH^-(aq) + H^+(aq) \rightarrow H_2O(l) \tag{4.3}$$

The stochiometry of these reactions tell us that one mole of acid, H^+, will neutralize one mole of OH^-.

If we react a known amount of sodium with water, we will produce its base, sodium hydroxide. If we then react a known amount of acid with this base, we can determine the number of moles of base produced by the sodium metal. Knowing the moles of base produced and the moles of initial sodium metal, we can readily calculate the number of OH^- produced for every mole of metal reacted with water. This allows us to write the chemical formula for the sodium hydroxide.

In this laboratory experiment, you are going to determine the identity of the metal ion in an unknown alkali metal hydroxide by reacting a known amount of unknown alkali metal hydroxide with a HCl soln. of known concentration. You will need to know the HCl soln. concentration very accurately to obtain good results. Consequently, you will perform an acid standardization and report the HCl soln. concentration to at least three significant figures.

In the standardization procedure, the HCl soln. is standardized against a material called tris-(hydroxymethyl)-aminomethane or (THAM). THAM, a weak base, is considered a primary standard for the standardization of dilute solutions of strong acids. It has a high equivalent mass and is highly purified, non-hygroscopic, and very soluble and colorless in soln. The reaction of THAM with acid is as follows:

$$H_2NC(CH_2OH)_3(aq) + H^+(aq) \rightarrow H_3NC(CH_2OH)_3^+(aq) \tag{4.4}$$

In titrating THAM, an indicator of Bromocresol green is used to estimate the end-point. Bromocresol green has a range of 3.8 to 5.4 (yellow to blue); end-point of THAM = $4.5 - 5.0$. Consequently, solution goes from a blue to a green color when the end-point of titration has been reached.

Use ACD/ChemSketch to draw the structural formula representation of equation (4.4), and then include the equation in the "Introduction" page of your ELN when discussing the neutralization reaction of THAM with HCl(aq).

Student Learning Outcomes: Upon completion of this laboratory experiment, students will be able to:

1. Standardize HCl for use in titrating an unknown alkali metal hydroxide solution.
2. Evaluate the precision of replicate titrations.

3. Determine the molar mass of an alkali metal hydroxide using acid-base titration.

4. Identify the alkali metal in an unknown alkali metal hydroxide.

5. Write the molecular equation for the reaction of the alkali metal hydroxide with acid.

SAFETY NOTE: *WEAR EYE PROTECTION AT ALL TIMES! Hydrochloric acid, HCl, is very corrosive and can cause severe burns if left in contact with the skin. Flush affected area with plenty of water; neutralize spills with sodium bicarbonate; Alkali hydroxides are very caustic, and potentially very hazardous to skin and eyes. In case of skin contact or eye contact, immediately flush with plenty of water for at least 15 minutes while removing contaminated clothing. Also, clean up any spills immediately; neutralize spills with dilute acetic acid, and DO NOT spill sample on the analytical balances.*

MATERIALS AND METHODS

Materials: Analytical balance, buret, glazed massing paper, Erlenmeyer flasks; bromocresol green indicator, carbon dioxide-free distilled water, 0.3 M HCl, unknown metal hydroxide, Tris-hydroxymethyl amino methane (THAM), 0.1% thymol blue indicator.

Methods

The experimental procedure for this experiment was developed, in part, by Engebretson, et al. (2014).[1]

Part 1. Standardization of 0.3 M HCl soln.

1. Zero an analytical balance and then accurately mass (±0.1 mg) a creased sheet of glazed massing paper and about 0.45–0.50 g (0.0001 g) of oven-dried (100°C for 1 hour) THAM (gross mass). Quantitatively transfer the THAM into a clean 250 mL Erlenmeyer flask, and then mass the sheet of glazed massing paper after sample transfer to obtain, by difference, the mass of the THAM (net mass).

2. Repeat step 1 two more times for a total a three trials. Be sure to record these masses to the correct number of significant figures in the "Data" section of your notebook.

3. Dissolve the THAM in 50 mL of CO_2-free distilled water.

4. Add 10 drops of the Bromocresol green indicator.

5. Fill your buret with the 0.3 *M* HCl soln. and prepare to titrate as you learned to do in Experiment 1 "Measurements and Volumetric Glassware."

6. Titrate the three base samples with the acid soln. with constant swirling. Be sure to record ALL buret readings, i.e., initial, final, and net volumes, to the correct level of significance. Recall that the solution goes from a blue to a green color when the end-point of titration has been reached.

7. Once you have titrated all three samples, and your precision appears reasonable, clean your flasks and go on to Part 2.

Part 2. Molar Mass of Alkali Metal in an Unknown Alkali Metal Hydroxide

1. Zero an analytical balance and then accurately mass (± 0.0001 g) a creased sheet of glazed massing paper and about 0.15–0.20 g (± 0.0001 g) of the unknown alkali metal hydroxide. Quantitatively transfer the metal hydroxide into a clean 125 mL Erlenmeyer flask, and then mass the sheet of glazed massing paper after sample transfer to obtain, by difference, the mass of the metal hydroxide transferred. **Caution: alkali hydroxides are very caustic, and potentially very hazardous to skin and eyes. In case of skin contact or eye contact immediately flush with plenty of water for at least 15 minutes while removing contaminated clothing. Also, clean up any spills immediately; neutralize spills with dilute acetic acid, and DO NOT spill sample on the analytical balances.**

2. Repeat step 1 two more times for a total a three trials. Be sure to record these masses to the correct number of significant figures in the "Data" section of your notebook.

3. Add about 50 mL of distilled water to each flask, making sure to wash down any sample adhering to the inside walls of your flask. Swirl to dissolve all the metal hydroxide.

4. Once the metal hydroxide is completely dissolved, add 10 drops of 0.1% thymol blue indicator and titrate each sample to the end-point with constant swirling. The end-point is obtained when the solution goes from blue to yellow and remains yellow for at least 1 minute. A pink or red color indicates a gross overrun of the end-point and a rerun would be required. Be sure to record ALL buret readings, i.e., initial, final, and net volumes, to the correct level of significance.

5. When all titrations are finished, drain your buret into a waste beaker and neutralize any excess HCl. Please pour your titrated samples containing the thymol blue indicator into the appropriately labeled container located in the recovered chemical fume hood.

Calculations

Part 1. Standardization of 0.3 M HCl soln.

1. Using the mass of THAM, the molar mass of THAM (121.14 g mol^{-1}), the stochiometric relationship in equation (4.4), and your net titrant volume, calculate the molar concentration (mol HCl L^{-1}) of your HCl soln. for each replicate and report the concentration at the correct level of significance.

2. Calculate the average HCl concentration, standard deviation, s, and the coefficient of variation (CV). The average, standard deviation, and the CV are calculated using equations (4.5), (4.6), and (4.7), respectively.

$$\overline{X} = \left(\frac{\sum X_i}{N}\right) \tag{4.5}$$

$$s = \sqrt{\frac{\sum_{i=1}^{N}(X_i - \overline{X})^2}{N - 1}} \tag{4.6}$$

$$C.V. = \left(\frac{s}{\overline{X}}\right)(100) \tag{4.7}$$

where $\overline{X}$ is the mean, X_i is the acid concertation for each trial, and N is the number of trials (i.e., $N = 3$).

The CV, also called the relative standard deviation (RSD), is a useful statistical measure of precision. A CV less than 5% is considered good under laboratory conditions. Your CV should be $\leq 5\%$.

Part 2. Determination of Alkali Metal in an Unknown Alkali Metal Hydroxide

1. Using the stoichiometry of the balanced equation [equation (4.8)] where X = alkali metal cation, your mass of unknown alkali metal hydroxide, and the net volume of HCl delivered, determine the moles of unknown metal hydroxide for each trial as indicated in equation (4.9), below.

$$XOH(aq) + HCl(aq) \rightarrow XCl(aq) + H_2O(l) \tag{4.8}$$

$$mol\ XOH = L\ of\ HCl\left(\frac{average\ mol\ HCl}{L}\right)\left(\frac{1\ mol\ XOH}{1\ mol\ HCl}\right) \tag{4.9}$$

2. Determine the molar mass of the unknown alkali hydroxide for each trial by using equation (4.10), below.

$$molar\ mass\ of\ XOH = \left(\frac{grams\ of\ XOH}{mol\ XOH}\right) \tag{4.10}$$

3. Average your three molar masses.

4. Determine the alkali metal cation, X, by subtracting the molar mass of hydroxide (OH^-) from the average molar mass of XOH.

5. What is the identity of the alkali metal cation?

6. Write the balanced equation showing the neutralization reaction of your alkali metal hydroxide with HCl(aq).

Results

Construct a table(s) summarizing your acid standardization and alkali metal hydroxide titration results. The results should include HCl concentrations for each trail, the average concentration, and the relative statistical results. Also, include a summary of the titration results of the unknown alkali metal hydroxide, including molar masses for each trial, the average molar mass, and the identity of the alkali metal.

Discussion/Conclusion

As part of your discussion, you should interpret your results and relate them to the objectives of the experiment. Discuss relationships, generalizations, shortcomings, and difficulties of the experiment. Focus your discussion on the meaning of your findings, not to recapitulate them. How does the determined molar mass of the alkali metal compare to the actual mass as depicted on the periodic table? What are some possible explanations for any deviation from the expected?

Conclusions

Your conclusions should include the salient results of the experiment as related to the original student learning outcomes. For instance, conclude the average HCl concentration, your average molar mass of the unknown alkali metal hydroxide, the identity of the alkali metal cation, and the equation showing the acid/base neutralization reaction between your alkali metal hydroxide and HCl(aq).

REFERENCE

1. Engebretson, J.; Doyle, D.; Elzenga, J. *General Chemistry II Laboratory (Chem 232L) Open Inquiry* Experiments. Chemical Formula of Sodium Hydroxide by Titration. Southwest Minnesota State University: Marshall, MN, 2014; p. 7 (unpublished).

EXPERIMENT 5

Investigating Copper Reactions

INTRODUCTION

In this experiment, you will begin with the element copper, Cu, and carry out a series of chemical reactions, which transform Cu to alternate chemical forms. You will start with a *reduction/oxidation* reaction, and then progress through a *metathesis*, *decomposition*, *acid/base*, and finally another *reduction/oxidation* reaction, which upon completion, leaves your final product in its original, elemental form.

The first chemical reaction in this experiment is the transformation of elemental copper, $Cu(s)$, to its ionic form, $Cu^{2+}(aq)$. To accomplish this, students will

Source: Frank Schindler

add nitric acid (HNO_3) to a beaker containing a known mass of $Cu(s)$. Because elements below hydrogen in the activity series of metals in aqueous solutions are not oxidized by H^+, $Cu(s)$ does not react with H^+ from the HNO_3, but rather with the NO_3^- species. That is, NO_3^- is reduced to $NO(g)$ while the $Cu(s)$ is oxidized to $Cu^{2+}(aq)$.

The reaction that takes place can be written two different ways. The *molecular equation* representing the oxidation of $Cu(s)$ to Cu^{2+} is given in equation (5.1).

$$3Cu(s) + 8HNO_3(aq) \rightarrow 3Cu(NO_3)_2(aq) + 2NO(g) + 4H_2O(l) \tag{5.1}$$

Another way of writing the reaction recognizes the fact that ionic compounds in solution exist as separate ions, and the same is true of strong acids such as nitric acid. Equation (5.2) represents the *complete* or *total ionic equation*.

$$3Cu(s) + 8H^+(aq) + 8NO_3^-(aq) \rightarrow 3Cu^{2+}(aq) + 6NO_3^-(aq) + 2NO(g) + 4H_2O(l) \quad (5.2)$$

The nitric oxide gas (NO) that is produced is not observed in this experiment, because it almost instantly reacts with atmospheric oxygen to produce nitrogen dioxide:

$$2NO(g) + O_2(g) \rightarrow 2NO_2(g) \quad (5.3)$$

The reaction involving copper is an example of a *reduction/oxidation* reaction. When an element increases in charge, it is said to be **oxidized**. In solution, most ions are colorless. Copper(II) ion, however, is an exception.

Sodium hydroxide is a strong base, which can neutralize acids. The solution made from the oxidation of Cu(s) to Cu^{2+} in the first transformation contains excess nitric acid and is thus, strongly acidic. The excess acid must be removed by adding sodium hydroxide. Once the excess acid is consumed, excess sodium hydroxide can react with the copper compound forming an insoluble precipitate, thus progressing the copper through a second transformation. This is an example of a *metathesis* reaction and is represented as:

$$Cu(NO_3)_2(aq) + 2NaOH(aq) \rightarrow Cu(OH)_2(s) + 2NaNO_3(aq) \quad (5.4)$$

The hydroxide ion is OH^- and the oxide ion is O^{2-}. Ionic compounds made from these ions are often closely related. If you consider the formula of copper(II) hydroxide and remove from it, one O atom and two H atoms, i.e., one water molecule, what remains is the formula for copper(II) oxide. Copper(II) hydroxide can, therefore, be called a "hydrate" of copper(II) oxide. In this case, heating the hydroxide is able to drive off the water from the solid, creating the oxide. This is accomplished even though the entire process is carried out in the presence of water. The conversion of Copper(II) hydroxide to its anhydrous, copper(II) oxide form, is an example of a *decomposition* reaction, which is represented by equation (5.5), and denotes the third copper transformation.

$$Cu(OH)_2(s) \rightarrow CuO(s) + H_2O(l) \quad (5.5)$$

Sulfuric acid is a strong acid, and in the right circumstances, can give up two H^+ ions. When it does, the sulfate ion remains. In the fourth transformation step, the hydrogen ions are taken up by the oxide ion, producing water as a product. The net overall reaction is

$$CuO(s) + H_2SO_4(aq) \rightarrow CuSO_4(aq) + H_2O(l) \quad (5.6)$$

This reaction is an example of an *acid/base* reaction. In such a reaction, a compound gives up H^+ ions to another compound. The substance giving up the H^+ ions is called the *acid* and substance accepting them is called the *base*.

In the first transformation of copper metal, the Cu(s) was oxidized from 0 charge to the +2 oxidation state. In the subsequent reactions, the copper atoms remained in the +2 state. To recover the copper metal, the copper ions must be returned to their native state of 0 charge. This is accomplished by adding electrons supplied by some element with a greater tendency to give up electrons than copper. Zinc is such an element. The net reaction in this case is more clearly written in net ionic form as

$$Cu^{2+}(aq) + Zn(s) \rightarrow Cu(s) + Zn^{2+}(aq) \tag{5.7}$$

expressing the fact that copper exists in solution as the copper(II) ion and that the negative ions, although present, play no real role in the overall reaction. Notice that the electrons required for the reduction of copper ions come from zinc atom. For copper, this reaction represents the opposite of the oxidation that takes place in the first step. This is called *reduction* and we say that the copper(II) ion is *reduced* to copper metal by the zinc. In this same reaction, we can also say that zinc is oxidized to its +2 state. We also refer to zinc as a *more active* metal than copper because it is more easily oxidized.

There is a secondary reaction taking place as well in this step and it is also related to the fact that zinc is more easily oxidized than copper. Since the formation of copper(II) sulfate took place in the presence of excess acid, there is a significant amount of H^+ ion present in the solution. Besides being an acid, H^+ ion can also act as an oxidizing agent, accepting electrons from another element, and producing hydrogen gas (H_2). In this secondary reaction, zinc is oxidized by the hydrogen ion according to equation (5.8).

$$Zn(s) + 2H^+(aq) \rightarrow Zn^{2+}(aq) + H_2(g) \tag{5.8}$$

Notice that this reaction competes with the first one for the zinc metal and, thereby works against the overall goal of reducing copper to its metallic state. However, with the directions given in this procedure, we should still see most of the copper ion reduced even in the presence of this competing reaction.

This laboratory experiment was designed for students to observe various types of chemical reactions and relate observations to these reactions, reinforce the idea of atoms being preserved in chemical reactions, and practice quantitative techniques by attempting to recover the original copper and computing the percent recovered.

Please note that in their pure forms, all of the compounds observed are solids. In this experiment, we may not see them as solids, because they may be dissolved in water. Water is present from the first step until the recovered copper is dried in the last step. In making observations, it is important to distinguish between a solution and a solid suspended in water.

Students need to prepare "Purpose" and "Materials and Methods" or "Procedures" sections of their notebook prior to laboratory. All requested observations and/or questions associated with this laboratory experiment should be written in the "Data" section of the notebook. You should also include balanced chemical equations for each step.

Student Learning Outcomes: Upon completion of this laboratory experiment, students will be able to:

1. Cycle copper metal through a variety of chemical reactions.
2. Identify the form of copper and of the reactants and products at various stages of the copper cycle, and write balanced molecular equations for each step.
3. Calculate percentage of copper recovered.

SAFETY NOTE: *Concentrated nitric acid, HNO₃, is hazardous. It produces severe burns on the skin, and its vapor irritates the lungs. Handle the* HNO_3 *in the fume hood and wear safety goggles; Sodium hydroxide, NaOH is very corrosive to the skin and especially dangerous if splashed in the eyes—wear safety goggles at all times! Methanol is extremely flammable and its vapors are toxic. Keep methanol away from open flames and use in the fume hood; Place recovered zinc sulfate, zinc chloride, and methanol in the "recovered chemicals" container located in the fume hood; Bunsen burners can reach extreme temperatures, e.g., 900–1,600°C depending on fuel mixture; Use burners with caution; All long hair needs to be pinned back.*

MATERIALS AND METHODS

Materials: Bunsen burner, ring stand, wire mesh, copper wire, wire shears, sandpaper, conc. Nitric acid (HNO₃), 3.0 *M* sodium hydroxide (NaOH), 6.0 *M* sulfuric acid (H₂SO₄), powdered zinc metal, 6 *M* HCl, methanol, and porcelain evaporating dish.

Methods

The experimental procedure of this experiment is adapted from "A cycle of copper reactions," from Chemistry in the Laboratory, James M. Postma, Julian L. Roberts, Jr., and J. Leland Hollenberg, New York: W.H. Freeman and Company, 2000.[1]

Transformation 1. The Oxidation of Copper Metal by Nitric Acid

1. Cut a length of pure copper wire that weighs about 0.5 g (about a 10-cm length).
2. Polish it with a piece of sandpaper to remove any oxides or other coating. (Some copper wire may have a very thin plastic coating.)
3. Accurately mass the copper wire using the electronic analytical balance, i.e., mass the sample to ± 0.0001 g.
4. Coil the wire in a flattened position and place it in the bottom of a 250-mL beaker.
5. **This step must be done in a fume hood because of the possibility of noxious gas being produced.** Add 4.0 mL of concentrated nitric acid (a solution of HNO_3. Swirl the solution around in the beaker until the copper has completely dissolved. Add water until the beaker is about half full. The remainder of the experiment can be carried out at your lab bench.
6. Record all observations related to this transformation in your notebook.

Transformation 2. Formation of Copper(II) Hydroxide

1. While stirring the solution from transformation 1 with a glass rod, add 30 mL of 3.0 M NaOH.
2. Record all observations related to this transformation in your notebook.

~ CHECK PH

Transformation 3. Formation of Copper(II) Oxide

1. Stirring gently with a glass rod to prevent "bumping," heat the solution just barely to the boiling point over a Bunsen burner (see Bunsen burner set-up as demonstrated by instructor). You should see a distinct change in the appearance of the suspended material. Record all observations related to this transformation in your notebook.
2. When the transformation is complete, remove the beaker from the flame and continue stirring for a minute or so. Then allow the suspended material to settle.
3. *Decant* (pour off) the liquid on top. Be careful not to lose any of the settled solid. Note: Decantation is a technique used to separate mixtures or to separate two phases. In this experiment, you want to decant the top, liquid layer thereby removing it from the solid precipitate. Proper decantation, i.e., placing a stir rod on the lip of the beaker, allows the analyst to (1) direct the flow of liquid, and (2) minimize loss of liquid down the outside of beaker (Fig. 5.1).

FIGURE 5.1   Proper decantation technique used in separating two phases. The stirring rod serves two purposes: (1) it directs the flow of the decantate, and (2) it removes the remaining decantate on the spout of the beaker. This can be critical in quantitative analysis where the analyst needs to ensure complete transfer of liquid and thus, no loss down the outside of the beaker. *Source: Frank Schindler*

4. Without stirring, add about 200 mL of hot distilled water, allow to settle again, and then decant. The purpose of the final rinsing and decanting process is to remove excess sodium, nitrate, and hydroxide ions from the mixture, leaving you with only a suspension of the solid in water.

Transformation 4. Formation of Copper(II) Sulfate

1. Add 15 mL of 6.0 M H_2SO_4 to the beaker containing the copper(II) oxide while stirring.
2. Record all observations related to this transformation in your notebook.

Transformation 5. Formation of Metallic Copper

1. In the fume hood, add 2.0 g of powdered zinc metal, stirring until any reaction is apparently complete.
2. Record all observations related to this transformation in your notebook.

Purification and Recovery of Copper Metal

1. Decant the liquid from transformation 5. Add 10 mL of 6 M HCl and warm, but do not boil the solution. The purpose of this step is to oxidize any remaining zinc metal in order to remove it. You may see the production of bubbles of hydrogen gas as this is taking place.

Note on the oxidation of Zn(s): Adding HCl allows us to recover purified copper by oxidizing excess zinc metal from the product mixture to its soluble Zn^{2+} form, which then can be rinsed away. In this last step, the HCl is added in excess to ensure this process goes to near completion. All that remains is solid copper and a number of ionic impurities all of which are dissolved in the water which remains.

2. When hydrogen evolution is apparently complete, decant the supernatant liquid, and transfer the copper to a porcelain evaporating dish. Use a spatula or rubber policeman.

3. Wash the copper with a small amount of distilled water, allow it to settle, and decant the wash water. Repeat the washing and decanting two more times. The rinsing and decanting steps help remove the ionic impurities from the copper product.

4. Move to the hood, away from all flames, and wash and decant several times with small amounts of methanol. Methanol will aid in the removal of water and is much more likely to evaporate completely, because of its relatively high volatility. Dispose of decanted methanol in the properly labeled container located in the fume hood.

5. Dry the copper product by placing the porcelain dish atop a beaker of boiling water. The beaker should contain boiling chips to effect smoother boil. Your instructor will demonstrate the set-up.

6. Mass an empty beaker, transfer the purified copper metal into the beaker and mass again.

7. When the recovered copper has been properly massed, place it in the appropriately labeled recovered chemical beaker located in the recovered chemical fume hood.

Calculations

Compare the final mass to the initial mass of copper used. Determine the percent recovery using equation (5.9).

$$\text{Percentage recovery} = \frac{\text{mass of recovered copper}}{\text{initial mass of copper wire}} \times 100 \qquad (5.9)$$

This calculation should be shown in the "Calculation" section of your notebook.

Results

In this experiment, you saw different forms of the element copper, and experienced the reactions associated with each transformation. Summarize the results and your observations by filling out a Results Summary table such as that shown for Table 5.1. Include your percentage recovery of the original copper and all molecular equations (use the Equation Editor function of Microsoft OneNote™).

TABLE 5.1   Summary of observations and salient results for the "cycle of copper" experiment.

Substance	Formula	Appearance (Color)	Water soluble? (Yes/No)	Molecular equation for substance formation
		Observations		
Copper(II) nitrate				
Copper(II) hydroxide				
Copper(II) oxide				
Copper(II) sulfate				
Copper metal				
		Results		
Mass of recovered copper, g				
Percentage recovery, %				

Discussion/Conclusions

As part of your discussion, answer the following questions related to each transformation and your percent copper recovery.

Transformation 1. The oxidation of copper metal by nitric acid. (1) What element was oxidized? (2) What observations did you make about nitrogen dioxide gas? (3) Where was the original copper after the reaction? (4) Was copper(II) nitrate soluble or insoluble?

Transformation 2. Formation of copper(II) hydroxide. (1) Was copper(II) hydroxide soluble or insoluble? (2) How could you tell? (3) What color was copper(II) hydroxide?

Transformation 3. Formation of copper(II) oxide. (1) What color was copper(II) oxide? (2) Is it soluble or insoluble?

Transformation 4. Formation of copper(II) sulfate. (1) What was the acid and what was the base in this reaction? (2) Was the copper(II) sulfate product soluble or insoluble? (3) What color was copper(II) sulfate? (4) Did the copper change its charge in this reaction?

Transformation 5. Formation of metallic copper. (1) What did you observe that indicated copper(II) ion was being consumed in this step? (2) What did you observe that indicated copper metal was being formed? (3) What did you observe that indicated a second reaction was taking place (in which the zinc is oxidized by hydrogen ion and making hydrogen gas)?

As a final discussion question, what percent of the original copper did you recover in the end? If this amount was not equal to 100%, to what do you attribute the difference?

Your conclusion should summarize the experiment and relate your observations and results to the original student learning outcomes. Your conclusions should include your percentage recovery of copper and speculation of recovery shortcomings and/or discrepancies.

REFERENCE

1. Postma, J. M.; Roberts, J. L., Jr.; Hollenberg, J. L. *Chemistry in the Laboratory*. A cycle of copper reactions. W.H. Freeman and Company: New York, 2000.

EXPERIMENT 6

Introduction to Calorimetry

INTRODUCTION

Thermochemistry deals with the relationship between chemical reactions and thermal energy changes. Under constant pressure, the changes in thermal energy or heats of reaction are called the enthalpy change, ΔH or ΔH_{rxn}. An exothermic reaction is one where the system, i.e., chemical reaction, produces or loses heat to the surroundings and its ΔH_{rxn} is negative. Conversely, an endothermic reaction is one where the system absorbs or gains heat from the surroundings and its ΔH_{rxn} is positive.[1]

Calorimetry is a method of determining heats of reaction. The heat generated by a reaction causes the temperature of a solution to rise. By measuring this temperature change, and relating it to the heat capacity, one can find the amount of heat generated in a reaction.

A "calorimeter" is an insulated device in which the reaction is carried out. In this experiment, the

Source: Frank Schindler

calorimeter is simply a pair of nested styrofoam cups with loose fitting lids. You will use two such calorimeters with one designated as the "master." Ideally, the calorimeter itself does not absorb any of the reaction heat. In practice, however, one needs to correct the observed temperature change for the fact that some of the heat is lost in this manner.

This laboratory introduces students to the theory of calorimetry, and provides an opportunity for them to manipulate a simple calorimeter to measure heat flow, and characterize the energy change of two common reactions. One is the reaction of a strong acid with a strong base, and the other is the oxidation of magnesium metal by a strong acid. The molecular and net ionic equations for these two reactions are depicted in equations (6.1) through (6.4).

$$NaOH(aq) + HCl(aq) \rightarrow H_2O(l) + NaCl(aq) \tag{6.1}$$

$$H^+(aq) + OH^-(aq) \rightarrow H_2O(l) \tag{6.2}$$

$$Mg(s) + 2HCl(aq) \rightarrow MgCl_2(aq) + H_2(g) \tag{6.3}$$

$$Mg(s) + 2H^+(aq) \rightarrow Mg^{2+}(aq) + H_2(g) \tag{6.4}$$

Student Learning Outcomes: Upon completion of this laboratory experiment, students will be able to:

1. Determine heat capacity of the calorimeter, C_{cal}.
2. Determine heat of reaction of a strong acid and a strong base.
3. Determine heat of reaction of magnesium with strong acid.
4. Compare experimental values of $\Delta H°_{rxn}$ using the standard enthalpies of formation, $\Delta H°_f$.

SAFETY NOTE: *WEAR EYE PROTECTION AT ALL TIMES! Sodium hydroxide, NaOH, and hydrochloric acid, HCl, are very corrosive. Both can cause severe burns if left in contact with the skin. Flush affected area with plenty of water; neutralize spills with sodium bicarbonate; discard neutralized solns. down drain; Do not touch the magnesium metal with your hands. Always use forceps when handling metals; Bunsen burners can reach extreme temperatures, e.g., 900–1,600°C depending on fuel mixture; Use burners with caution; All long hair needs to be pinned back; All chemicals can be disposed of down the drain except methanol, which should be properly disposed of in the hazardous waste container located in the fume hood. Always use methanol in the fume hood and away from open flames.*

MATERIALS AND METHODS

Materials: Four styrofoam cups with lids, thermometer, top-loading balance, Bunsen burner, ring stand, wire mesh, 1.0 M sodium hydroxide (NaOH), 1.0 M HCl, magnesium metal, and methanol.

Methods

Part 1. Finding the Heat Capacity of the Calorimeter

1. Begin heating some water (a bit more than 50 mL) in a beaker with a Bunsen burner.

2. Make two calorimeters, i.e., the "master" calorimeter and "calorimeter 2," by placing one styrofoam cup inside the other. Place the master calorimeter on the top-loading balance, zero or tare the balance, and then add 50 mL of distilled water. Adjust the amount of water with a disposable dropper pipette to exactly 50.00 g while the calorimeter is on the balance. Place a lid on the calorimeter and insert thermometer into center of lid.

3. When the water on the burner reaches about 60°C, measure 50 mL of the hot water into calorimeter 2, adjust the amount on the balance to exactly 50.00 g, and place a lid on the calorimeter; do not insert a thermometer in this calorimeter. Wait approximately 10 minutes for the temperatures of both to stabilize.

4. After temperature stabilization, record the temperatures of the master calorimeter, and then remove the thermometer from the master calorimeter and insert it into calorimeter number 2. After several minutes of temperature stabilization, record the temperature of calorimeter 2.

5. Now, carefully and quickly pour the entire contents of calorimeter number 2 (the hot calorimeter) into the master calorimeter (the cold one). Immediately replace the lid and the thermometer on the master calorimeter. Wait about 10 minutes for the temperature to stabilize. Record the final temperature, T_{final}.

Part 2. The Heat of Reaction of a Strong Acid and a Strong Base

1. Set up both calorimeters. Add 50 mL of 1.0 M sodium hydroxide to one calorimeter and 50 mL of 1.0 M hydrochloric acid to the other. Use the balance to adjust the amounts to exactly 50.00 g just as you did in the first part. Allow both to equilibrate for about 10 minutes. They should both be at about room temperature. Record their temperatures and the average.

2. After the temperatures are stable, pour the contents of calorimeter 2 into the master calorimeter. Close it and allow 10 minutes for the temperature to stabilize. Record the final temperature after the appropriate stabilization time.

Part 3. The Heat of Reaction of Magnesium with Strong Acid

The experimental procedure for this part of the experiment was developed in part by Redemske et al. (2015).[2]

1. In this part of the experiment, you will use only the designated master calorimeter.

2. Begin with 100 mL of 1.0 M HCl in the calorimeter. Adjust the amount using a balance to be exactly 100.00 g of solution in the calorimeter. Set it up and allow it to equilibrate for 10 minutes as before. Record the initial temperature when stabilized.

NOTE: Magnesium metal undergoes passivation when exposed to air. That is, it reacts with atmospheric oxygen and nitrogen and develops a thin coating of MgO and Mg_3N_2. This coating needs to be removed, so it does not affect the mass of Mg(s), and thus the accuracy of the experiment.

3. To recondition the Mg(s), perform the following procedures:

    a. Add about 0.75 g of Mg(s) to 20 mL of 1.0 M HCl in a small beaker and allow the reaction to proceed to completion. The Mg(s) should have a shiny gray appearance.

    b. Decant the exhausted HCl solution into a waste beaker, and then proceed to rinse the reconditioned Mg(s) several times with 10 mL aliquots of distilled water, decanting each rinsate into the waste beaker. Discard waste beaker content down the drain.

    c. Move to the fume hood and away from open flames, and perform two final rinsings with 5 mL aliquots of methanol. Decant rinsate into a waste beaker. The methanol helps remove water and dry the Mg(s).

    d. Place beaker containing reconditioned Mg(s) on hot plate and dry. Make sure to dispose of waste beaker containing the methanol rinsate into the appropriately labeled recovered chemicals container located in the fume hood.

4. Accurately mass all the reconditioned Mg(s) on the analytical balance. The Mg(s) in this experiment is the limiting reactant, and determines the stoichiometry of the reaction. The acid will be present in excess.

5. Quickly add the reconditioned Mg(s) to the calorimeter containing the 100.00 g of 1.0 M HCl you prepared in step 2 and close it. There should be an immediate reaction. Wait for the reaction to run and for the system to reach equilibrium, i.e., approximately 10 minutes. Record the final temperature.

6. Slowly add baking soda to the calorimeter to effect complete neutralization of any excess acid; discard contents down the drain.

Calculations

Part 1. Finding the Heat Capacity of the Calorimeter

In Part 1 of this experiment, you collected the data needed to determine the heat capacity of your master calorimeter. You started with a master calorimeter containing 50.00 g of "cold" water and calorimeter 2 containing 50.00 g of "hot" water. In an ideal situation, we would expect mixing two identical masses of water would result in a new mixture with an equilibrated temperature that is the average of the two initial temperatures. It will not quite do that, however, because the calorimeter absorbs some heat, and the temperature will actually be lower than what we expect. The object here is to determine how much.

1. Determine the average of the two temperatures using equation (6.5). This is the "ideal" or theoretical temperature. You should have observed something slightly less than this.

$$\text{Expected Average Temperature} = \frac{T_{\text{master calorimeter water}} + T_{\text{calorimeter 2 water}}}{2} \qquad (6.5)$$

2. Using equation (6.6), determine the change in temperature, ΔT, of the master calorimeter contents by subtracting the expected average temperature, T_{expected} from the final temperature, T_{final}, of your hot water/cold water mixture. For example, if your expected average is 40°C and you measured a final temperature of 35°C, then the difference or $\Delta T = -5$°C. Your change in temperature of the master calorimeter contents must be negative. If not, something is wrong.

$$\Delta T = T_{\text{final}} - T_{\text{expected}} \qquad (6.6)$$

The water must have lost a certain amount of heat to account for the difference. This heat must have gone into the calorimeter. The amount of heat absorbed by the master calorimeter can be calculated using the specific heat of water, which is 4.18 J K^{-1} g^{-1}. Multiplying water's specific heat by the mass of 100 mL (100.00 g) of water, we find its heat capacity to be 418 J K^{-1}. The heat lost by the water is, therefore $= (\Delta T)$ (418 J K^{-1}), a negative number. The heat gained by the calorimeter is simply the opposite of this, a positive number. For example, with a temperature difference of -5°C, the heat absorbed by the calorimeter will be 2090 J. Recall a unit change in K $=$ a unit change in °C, so 418 J K$^{-1} =$ 418 J °C^{-1}.

Use equation (6.7) to determine the heat absorbed by calorimeter.

$$\text{Heat absorbed by calorimeter} = (\Delta T)\left(\frac{418 \text{ J}}{\text{K}}\right) \tag{6.7}$$

3. Now we must calculate the heat capacity of the calorimeter, C_{cal}. As the hot water was added, the calorimeter temperature increased from that of the cold water to the final temperature, T_{final}. For example, if the cold water was originally at 25°C and the final temperature you recorded above is 35°C, then the change in temperature of the calorimeter was $\Delta T_{cal} = +10°C$. The heat capacity of the calorimeter is simply the heat absorbed by the calorimeter, as determined from equation (6.7) above, divided by ΔT_{cal}. For example, if the heat absorbed by the calorimeter is 2090 J, and the ΔT_{cal} is 10°C, then the heat capacity of the calorimeter, C_{cal}, is 209 J deg^{-1}.

Use equation (6.8) to determine the heat capacity of the calorimeter, C_{cal}.

$$C_{cal} = \left(\frac{\text{Heat absorbed by calorimeter, J}}{\Delta T_{cal}}\right) \tag{6.8}$$

The heat capacity of the calorimeter and the heat capacity of water constitutes the heat capacity of the surroundings, C_{surr}. This value used in the subsequent sections is simply the sum of the heat capacity of 100 mL of water and that of the calorimeter, or $C_{surr} = (418 \text{ J deg}^{-1} + C_{cal})$. This assumes you are using 100.00 g of water.

Part 2. The Heat of Reaction of a Strong Acid and a Strong Base

In your experimental setup, the ΔH_{rxn} of any reaction is calculated using the heat capacity of the surroundings, C_{surr}, you determined in Part 1 and the change in temperature of the reaction mixture. Therefore the heat of reaction is:

$$\Delta H_{rxn} = -(C_{surr})(T_{final} - T_{initial}) = -(C_{surr})(\Delta T) \tag{6.9}$$

The minus sign arises from the fact that an increase in the heat content of the water and the calorimeter (the surroundings) results from a decrease in the enthalpies of the reacting substances (the system). It is simply that ΔH for an exothermic reaction is negative.

1. Compute your ΔT. Also, determine ΔH_{rxn} using equation (6.9).
2. Using the balanced molecular or net ionic equation, (6.1) or (6.2), determine the number of moles of reactants and products from the concentrations and the volumes used, i.e., moles H^+ = moles OH^- = moles H_2O = (1.0 mol L^{-1}) × (0.05000 L).
3. Find the heat of reaction by dividing your measured ΔH_{rxn} by the number of moles of water, and report your answer in kJ mol^{-1} of water produced.

Part 3. The Heat of Reaction of Magnesium with Strong Acid

1. Compute your ΔT. Also, determine ΔH_{rxn} using equation (6.9).
2. Determine the number of moles of magnesium metal used.
3. Find the standard heat of reaction by dividing your measured ΔH_{rxn} by the number of moles of Mg(s) and report your answer in kJ mol^{-1}.

Finally, calculate the ΔH_{rxn} for the acid/base and the Mg/HCl reactions using the standard enthalpies of formation, ΔH_f°, and equation (6.10). The ΔH_f° of $MgCl_2$(aq) $= -769.9$ kJ mol^{-1}.

$$\Delta H_{rxn}^{\circ} = \Sigma n\Delta H_f^{\circ}(\text{products}) - \Sigma m\Delta H_f^{\circ}(\text{reactants}) \qquad (6.10)$$

Results

In this experiment, you determined the heat capacity of your coffee-cup calorimeter and the thermodynamic surroundings of your experimental setup. Summarize the results by tabulating the (1) heat capacity of the calorimeter and surroundings, (2) heat of reaction of a strong acid and a strong base, (3) heat of reaction of magnesium with strong acid, and (4) the heat of reactions for both reactions under standard conditions.

Discussions/Conclusions

Your conclusions should include: (1) heat capacity of the calorimeter, (2) heat of reaction of a strong acid and a strong base, (3) heat of reaction of magnesium with strong acid, and (4) the heat of reactions for both reactions under standard conditions. Discuss how your results compare to those calculated from the standard enthalpies of formation, ΔH_f°. Speculate on any discrepancies.

REFERENCES

1. Flowers, P.; Theopold, K.; Langley, R.; Robinson, W. *Chemistry*, OpenStax College. 2019. (https://openstax.org/details/books/chemistry-2e).
2. Redemske, B.; Petrowiak, C.; Peters, J. *General Chemistry II Laboratory (Chem 232L) Open Inquiry* Experiments. Cleaning the Oxide Coating off Solid Magnesium to get a More Accurate Heat of Reaction. Southwest Minnesota State University: Marshall, MN, 2015; p. 8 (unpublished).

EXPERIMENT 7

Emission and Absorption Spectroscopy

INTRODUCTION

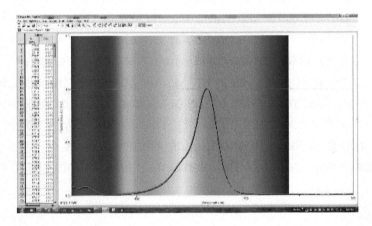

© Cora J. Engels

Spectroscopy is a scientific measurement technique used to study the interaction of electromagnetic radiation with matter. Spectroscopy measures electromagnetic radiation that is emitted, absorbed, or scattered by matter, and is used extensively in chemistry to qualify and quantity chemical species. Spectroscopy also aids in determining "molecular structures accurately, rapidly, and nondestructively using very small quantities of material."[1]

Emission spectroscopy deals with the emission of radiant energy (or light) from atoms in an excited electronic state. The emission of radiation from a particular source may be *monochromatic* (a single wavelength) or *polychromatic* (many different wavelengths). When the radiation emitted from some source is separated into its component wavelengths by passing the light through a prism, a *spectrum* is produced.[2] If a spectrum contains only specific wavelengths, it is called a *line spectrum*. Conversely, if a spectrum contains all wavelengths, it is called a *continuous spectrum*. Light from the sun, stars, and/or incandescent light bulbs are examples of radiation sources that produce a continuous spectrum. The light from these sources appear white, because all wavelengths of the visible spectrum, as well as wavelengths outside the visible spectrum, are emitted. The wavelengths of visible light include the shortest, most energetic radiation corresponding to the color violet and extending continuously through the longest, least energetic radiation, which corresponds to the color red. Figure 7.1 shows examples of continuous and line spectra.[3]

Since each type of atom is electronically unique, i.e., they each have a unique set of electrons and thus set of energy levels, each one displays a characteristic emission spectrum. For instance, when Na vapor under vacuum is exposed to high heat or voltage, electrons are excited from their ground state to a higher energy level. As the electrons return to their ground state, they emit a wavelength of radiation with energy corresponding to the difference between the allowable energy levels of transition. Since the emission of photonic energy corresponds to a particular wavelength of light, a characteristic color will be perceived as long as the emission is within the visible spectrum. In the case of the Na atom, more intense emission lines in the visible portion of the spectrum are observed at about 590 nm when electrons relax to the ground state. This transition corresponds to the yellow sections of the spectrum (Fig. 7.1). This explains why some street lights containing Na vapor appear yellow. In short, each element emits its own set of colors, and these colors are as characteristic to the element as fingerprints are to humans.

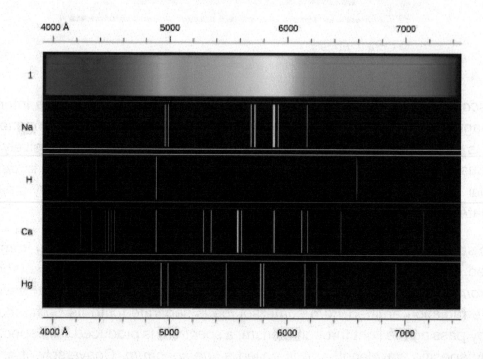

FIGURE 7.1   Compare the two types of emission spectra: continuous spectrum of white light (top) and the line spectra of the light from excited sodium, hydrogen, calcium, and mercury atoms.[3]
Source line: Download for free at https://openstax.org/details/books/chemistry-2e.

Johann Balmer derived an equation that relates the four visible emission lines of hydrogen (Fig. 7.1) to positive whole number integers, n_1 and n_2, where n_2 is larger or is of a higher energy than n_1.[2] Balmer's relationship was later generalized to include lines in the ultraviolet and infrared regions, and therefore used to calculate the wavelengths of all spectral lines of hydrogen. The generalized equation, called the *Rydberg equation*, is depicted in equation (7.1).

$$\frac{1}{\lambda} = R_\infty \left(\frac{1}{n_1^2} - \frac{1}{n_2^2} \right) \tag{7.1}$$

The whole number integer, n, later became known as the *principle quantum number*, and R_∞ is the *Rydberg constant* and is $1.096776 \times 10^7 \ \text{m}^{-1}$.

If electromagnetic radiation is emitted when an electron transitions from an initial, higher allowed energy state (n_2 or n_i) to a final, lower allowed energy state (n_1 or n_f), then the visible emission lines observed for the hydrogen atom will all involve $n_f = 2$. The series of visible emission lines generated via the electronic transitions from $n_i > 2$ to $n_f = 2$ in the hydrogen atom is called the *Balmer series*. The Rydberg equation when expressed in terms of the Balmer series is:

$$\frac{1}{\lambda} = R_\infty \left(\frac{1}{2^2} - \frac{1}{n_i^2} \right) \tag{7.2}$$

and it follows by expressing the Rydberg equation in the form of the straight line model

$$\frac{1}{\lambda} = -R_\infty \frac{1}{n_i^2} + R_\infty \left(\frac{1}{2^2} \right) \tag{7.3}$$

and plotting $\frac{1}{\lambda}$ as a function of $\frac{1}{n_i^2}$ produces a slope $= -R_\infty$.

The concept of emission spectra will be explored in this laboratory by performing flame tests on several different metal chloride salts, observing line spectra of different gases, and verifying the Rydberg constant.

Absorption spectroscopy is the most common form of spectroscopy.[1] The basis of absorption spectroscopy is that matter, i.e., atoms or molecules in their ground electronic state, absorb electromagnetic radiation, and the amount absorbed is a function of the wavelength, λ, of the radiation. Matter may absorb radiation in the nonvisible range of the electromagnetic spectrum, i.e., ultraviolet and shorter wavelengths or infrared and longer wavelengths, or in the visible range, i.e., 400–750 nm.[2] It is when matter absorbs or emits radiation in the visible range that our eyes perceive color.

A compound or a solution has a particular color for one of two reasons: (1) it reflects or transmits light of that color, or (2) it absorbs light of the complimentary color (Fig. 7.2).[3] For example, Fig. 7.3 shows the absorption spectrum of a blue-colored solution. With this particular solution, the maximum absorbance takes place at a wavelength, λ_{max} = about 630 nm. Because the solution absorbs in this region of visible light, our eyes will perceive the complementary or blue color, i.e., the color diametrically opposite in the color wheel (Fig. 7.2). Moreover, note the absorption spectrum of Fig. 7.3 shows little absorption of light from the blue end of the spectrum further suggesting the solution is perceived blue in color. It is

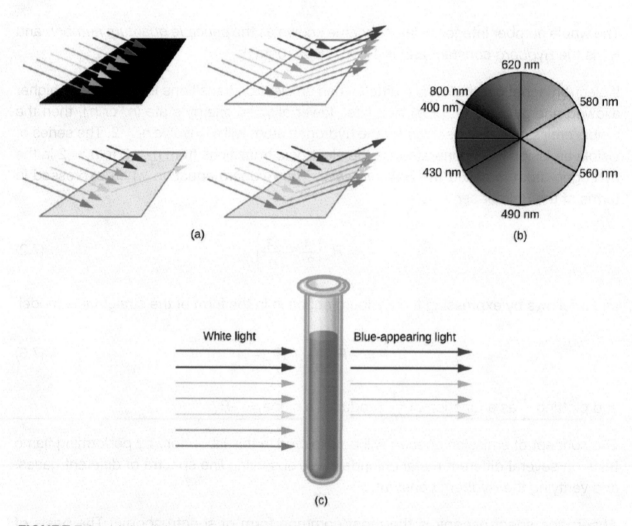

FIGURE 7.2   (a) An object appears black if it absorbs all colors of visible light, and it appears white if it reflects all colors of visible light. An object has a color if it absorbs all colors except one, such as this yellow strip. The strip also appears yellow if it absorbs the complementary color from white light (in this case, indigo). (b) Complementary colors are located directly across from one another on the color wheel. (c) A solution of $[Cu(NH_3)_4]^{2+}$ ions absorbs red and orange light, so the transmitted light appears as the complementary color, blue. This figure and caption was excerpted from Flowers et al. (2019).[3] *Source line: Download for free at https://openstax.org/details/books/chemistry-2e*

important to note that usually a range of photons are absorbed, representing a range of colors, and that the color we perceive is a blend of the colors of the photons transmitted.

This laboratory experiment introduces students to the fundamental concepts of emission and absorption spectroscopy, and provides an opportunity for students to use one type of modern instrumentation used in a chemical and/or biological laboratory setting.

Student Learning Outcomes: Upon completion of this laboratory experiment, students will be able to:

1. Perform flames test on several different metal chloride salts and relate the color of emitted light to the position of the visible spectrum.
2. View the emission spectra of hydrogen and mercury atoms using a voltage source and spectroscope.
3. Evaluate wavelengths of the visible emission lines of hydrogen to determine the value of the Rydberg constant and then compare experimental to the accepted value.
4. Use Logger Pro 3 software and Vernier® SpectroVis Plus Spectrophotometer to evaluate the absorption spectra of transparent samples of common food dyes.

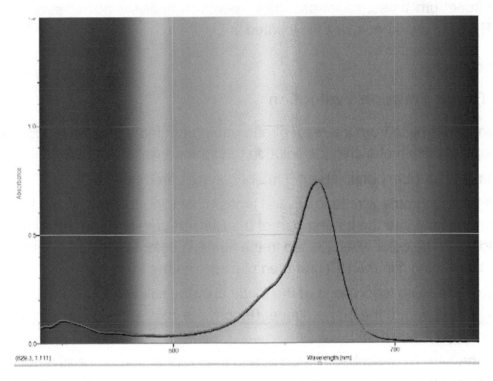

FIGURE 7.3   Absorption spectrum of a blue-colored solution as collected using Logger Pro 3 software and the Vernier® SpectroVis Plus Spectrophotometer.[4] *Source line: Download for free at https://openstax.org/details/books/chemistry-2e*

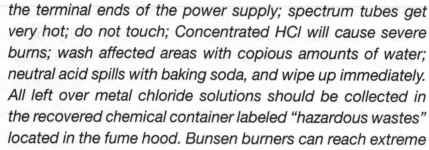

SAFETY NOTE: *The power supply used in this lab are 5000 volts and must be handled with extreme caution; do not touch the terminal ends of the power supply; spectrum tubes get very hot; do not touch; Concentrated HCl will cause severe burns; wash affected areas with copious amounts of water; neutral acid spills with baking soda, and wipe up immediately. All left over metal chloride solutions should be collected in the recovered chemical container labeled "hazardous wastes" located in the fume hood. Bunsen burners can reach extreme temperatures, e.g., 900–1,600°C depending on fuel mixture; Use burners with caution; All long hair needs to be pinned back; <u>WEAR EYE PROTECTION AT ALL TIMES!</u>*

MATERIALS AND METHODS

Materials: Concentrated HCl; 1 M solutions of NaCl, CaCl$_2$, CuCl$_2$, BaCl$_2$, LiCl, SrCl$_2$, and KCl; red, green, blue, and yellow food dyes diluted to $A_{max} = 1$; *Logger Pro 3* software on your laptop; Vernier® SpectroVis Plus Spectrophotometer or Spectronic 20D+ spectrophotometer; Spot plates; nichrome wire loops; Bunsen burner; hydrogen and mercury spectrum tubes; spectroscopes, spectrum analysis power supply; Microsoft Excel®; Rydberg_workbook.xlsx file located in D2L.

Methods

Part 1. Flame Emission Evaluation

1. Obtain a spot plate from the reagent and equipment table, and then add about 10 drops of each metal chloride solution to separate wells.

2. In a small test tube, obtain about 5 mL of concentrated HCl(aq).

3. Clean your nichrome wire loop several times by placing the loop in the HCl and then placing the loop into the hottest part of the Bunsen burner flame. A clean wire loop should give little color when placed in the flame. If color is emitted, clean the loop again by swirling it in the HCl and then placing into the flame.

4. Immerse the clean loop in one of the metal chloride salt solutions and place the loop in the hottest part of the burner flame. Record the color of the flame in the "Data" section of your notebook.

5. Clean the loop as described in step 3, and then repeat step 4 for all remaining metal chloride solutions.

6. When all tests have been completed, thoroughly clean the nichrome loop as described in step 3, and then place the loop back on the reagent and equipment table. Neutralize excess acid with baking soda and then discard down the drain.

Part 2. Emission Spectra and Rydberg Constant

1. Obtain a spectroscope and verify the diffraction grating, which is a thin, round plastic disk, is located inside the eyepiece. The eyepiece is the end-cap with a round hole. The eyepiece end with diffraction grating is called the grating end of the spectroscope.

2. Ready the spectroscope for viewing emission spectra by holding the eyepiece or grating end of the spectroscope to your eye, and then, while aiming the spectroscope at a light source, rotate the cap at the grating end until a broad band of color appears parallel to the slit end. The continuous spectrum of light should resemble that in Fig. 7.1, and appear just to the right of the slit as you are looking through the tube. While holding the eyepiece and tube still, rotate the slotted end-cap to get the widest spectrum. The slit should be in a vertical position.

3. Turn the power on the spectrum analysis power supply, and aiming the spectroscope at the lamp, record the color of each emission line, the number of lines, the relative intensities of the lines, and draw the emission spectra for hydrogen and mercury in your notebook. The spectra should resemble those depicted in Fig. 7.1. Due to the limitations of the simple spectroscope, you may not see all visible emission lines.

CAUTION: The lamps may be extremely hot; do not touch the power supply terminals!

4. Go to Part 3. Complete steps 5, 6, and 7 of this Part 2 when you have completed the laboratory experiment.

5. Download the Excel® file titled "Rydberg_workbook.xlsx" located in D2L for this course.

6. Using the visible emission lines of the hydrogen atom as presented in the Excel workbook, determine the n_i value associated with each emission. Recall the visible emission lines observed by Balmer all involved $n_f = 2$.

7. Once determined, enter the series of n_i values into the respective cells of the workbook. If done correctly, the plot, which is produced automatically, will show a coefficient of determination, $R^2 = 1$. Proceed to calculate the Rydberg constant from the slope of the linear equation [equation (7.3)]. The slope of the equation has units of nm^{-1}, so you will need to convert this value to the more common Rydberg unit, m^{-1}.

Part 3. Absorption of Dyes

1. Install *Logger Pro 3* software on your laptop, and connect the *SpectroVis Plus* to your computer's USB port. You may need to include a password to execute installation. Your instructor will provide password if needed.

2. Prepare four dilute stock solutions, i.e., one for each food dye, blue, red, yellow, and green, by placing 1 drop of dye in a 100-mL graduated cylinder and then bringing to the 100.0 mL volume with distilled water. Cap the end of the cylinder and invert several times to ensure proper mixing. Pour the dilute solution into a test tube and save. Rinse the graduated cylinder and repeat for the remaining food dyes. You should have four test tubes each containing a different colored solution.

3. Calibrate the *SpectroVis Plus* by selecting **Calibrate**, then **Spectrometer** from the **Experiment** menu. Fill a curette about 3/4 full with distilled water and place it in the cuvette holder. Make sure you wipe your cuvette free of moisture and fingerprints using a Kimwipe prior to inserting into the cuvette holder. Follow the instructions in the dialog box to complete the calibration, and then click **OK**.

4. Following calibration, remove your blank cuvette and pour out the distilled water. Rinse the cuvette several times with a colored solution to condition the cuvette and prevent contamination and/or dilution. *Be sure to use the <u>same cuvette</u> for the blank and the colored solutions. Each cuvette has minor differences that can lead to significant errors if different cuvettes are used.*

5. Generate an *absorption spectrum* by filling the cuvette about 3/4 full with the colored solution. Wipe the cuvette with a Kimwipe and insert into cuvette holder of the *SpectroVis Plus*. Click **Collect**, [▶ Collect], to generate a spectrum. Once the absorption spectrum is visible, click **Stop** to end data collection.

6. Position your mouse cursor at the highest part of the absorption spectrum. You should see the *x* and *y* coordinates given in parentheses in lower left corner of the absorption spectrum. Move your cursor along the curve until maximum absorbance, A_{max}, is reached. Record the wavelength at this point in your notebook. This is the λ_{max}. Alternatively, look at the data tabulated to the left of the screen and select λ_{max}.

7. Highlight the absorption spectrum with a left mouse click. Select copy, and then paste the spectrum in a Word® document. This figure can be printed later for inclusion in your notebook.

8. Remove the cuvette from the *SpectroVis Plus*, rinse with distilled water, and then rinse several times with the next colored solution to condition the cuvette and prevent contamination. Repeat steps 5–7 for this solution.

9. When the absorption spectrum for the second colored solution has been acquired and copied, remove the cuvette from the *SpectroVis Plus*, rinse with distilled water, and then rinse several times with the next colored solution to condition the cuvette and prevent contamination. Repeat steps 5–7 for this solution.

10. When the absorption spectrum for the third colored solution has been acquired and copied, remove the cuvette from the *SpectroVis Plus*, rinse with distilled water, and then rinse several times with the next, and final colored solution to condition the cuvette. Repeat steps 5–7 for this solution.

11. When this part of the experiment has been completed, rinse cuvettes with distilled water and place the *SpectroVis Plus* back in the box for storage. Clean all test tubes, and graduated cylinders. All dye solutions can go down the drain.

Part 3. Absorption of Dyes (Alternate Method)

Make up a single colored solution as outlined in Part 3, step 2 of the preceding method. Use a Spectronic 20D+ spectrophotometer to determine the absorption spectrum of this dye solution by doing the following:

1. Turn the power on and allow the instrument to warm-up for 10 to 15 minutes.
2. Set the instrument to Transmittance (T) mode.
3. Set the wavelength on the instrument to 350 nm.
4. With the sample holder empty, adjust the T to read zero.
5. Place a cuvette containing a blank sample (distilled water) in the instrument and adjust the instrument to read 100% T. BE SURE that the cuvette has been wiped free of any liquid and/or finger prints with a Kim wipe.
6. Set the instrument to Absorbance (A) mode; the instrument should read 0 A.
7. Remove the blank and insert your sample cuvette. BE SURE that the cuvette has been wiped free of any liquid and/or fingerprints with a Kim wipe.
8. Read and record the absorbance of the sample.
9. Remove your sample cuvette and increase the wavelength by 10 nm. Re-insert the blank and close the holder door, and then re-adjust the instrument to read zero absorbance.
10. Remove the blank and insert your sample cuvette again. BE SURE that the cuvette has been wiped free of any liquid and/or fingerprints with a Kim wipe.
11. Read and record the absorbance of the sample at this new wavelength.
12. Repeat steps 9 though 11 until you have recorded the absorbance at each wavelength interval up to 750 nm.
13. Copy and paste (paste as: "Match Destination Formatting (M)" from the "Paste Options" command) your A and wavelength data from OneNote® into MS Excel®. Plot A (y axis) vs. wavelength (x axis) and determine the absorption maximum.
14. Copy and paste your graph into OneNote®.

Calculations

There are few calculations associated with this laboratory experiment. Most calculations have been performed for you in the Excel® workbook titled "Rydberg_workbook.xlsx". You will need to convert the Rydberg constant from nm^{-1} to m^{-1} using the correct conversion factor.[2,3]

Results

Construct a table(s) summarizing your salient results from each part of this laboratory experiment. Results should include the observed colors of the metal chloride salts, the colors observed from the emission spectra of hydrogen and mercury, the graph of $1/\lambda$ as a function of $1/n_i^2$, the linear equation and R^2 for the Rydberg constant determination, the experimental Rydberg constant, and copies of your absorption spectra with the λ_{max} for each colored solution.

Discussion/Conclusions

Interpret your results and relate them to the objectives of the experiment. Discuss relationships, generalizations, shortcomings, and difficulties of the experiment. Discussion should focus on the meaning of your findings, and address the following topics:

1. Describe how the flame emission test could be used in analytical chemistry.

2. Why does the glow of hydrogen appear blue? What color would sodium and argon emit?

3. Relate the absorption spectra determined in Part 3 to the λ_{max} and the color perceived from the dye solutions. Does the color you perceive the solutions to be agree with your data? Explain.

4. A solution of $[Ti(H_2O)_6]_2^{3+}$ absorbs much of the yellow, green, and blue, but little red and violet wavelengths of the visible spectrum. The λ_{max} for this chemical species = 500 nm. Given this description, sketch the absorption spectrum of a solution of $[Ti(H_2O)_6]_2^{3+}$. What color would you expect this solution to appear? How would the absorption spectrum change if you decreased the concentration of the $[Ti(H_2O)_6]_2^{3+}$, i.e., if you diluted the sample with water?

Your conclusions should include the salient results of the experiment and interpreted in the context of the original student learning outcomes.

REFERENCES

The opening image is a screen shot from a student's computer when using SpectroVis Plus Spectrophotometer.[4]

1. Loudon, G. M. *Organic Chemistry*, 4th ed.; Oxford University Press: New York, 2002.

2. Brown, T. L.; Lemay, E. H., Jr.; Bursten, B. E.; Murphy, C. J.; Woodard, P. M.; M. W. Stoltzfus. *Chemistry: The Central Science*, 13th ed.; Pearson Education, Inc.: New Jersey, 2015.

3. Flowers, P.; Theopold, K.; Langley, R.; Robinson, W. *Chemistry*, OpenStax College. 2019. (https://openstax.org/details/books/chemistry-2e).

4. Vernier®. *SpectroVis Plus Spectrophotometer*; Operator's manual. Beaverton, OR, 2012.

Synthesis and Analysis of Alum, KAl(SO₄)₂•12H₂O

INTRODUCTION

Alum is a solid ionic compound with many uses. It is used as an astringent to prevent bleeding from small cuts, as an ingredient in deodorants, as an ingredient in baking powders, and as a preservative used in pickling. Alum is also used in purification of drinking water in industries. For instance, alum is used to clarify water by neutralizing the electrical double layer surrounding very fine suspended particles, allowing them to flocculate (stick together). After flocculation, the particles are large enough to settle out of solution and are more easily removed.

Source: Frank Schindler

The formula of alum is $KAl(SO_4)_2 \cdot 12H_2O$ and the standard name is potassium aluminum sulfate dodecahydrate. It is an unusual ionic compound in that it includes two positive ions, K^+ and Al^{3+}. It also includes 12 water molecules in each formula unit, which remain in the solid when it is precipitated from a water solution. Such water molecules are referred to as "waters of hydration" and ionic compounds which incorporate them into their solid structures are called "hydrates." Many solid ionic compounds exist as hydrates. It is important to include these water molecules in the formula mass of the compound when doing stoichiometric calculations.

The synthesis of alum in this experiment is carried out beginning with aluminum from aluminum cans. This is not how alum is produced commercially. Aluminum does not occur in nature as the native metal and it is very costly to produce. Thus, the commercial production of alum begins with minerals containing aluminum in its oxidized state rather than elemental aluminum.

Oxidation of aluminum. The primary chemical change happening in the first reaction is the oxidation of aluminum, Al(s), to aluminum ion by water, Al^{3+}(aq). Aluminum, like the alkali metals and alkaline earth metals, is a very active metal, which can be oxidized by water. For aluminum, a balanced reaction is:

$$2Al(s) + 6H_2O(l) \rightarrow 2Al^{3+}(aq) + 6OH^-(aq) + 3H_2(g) \tag{8.1}$$

The situation is actually a bit more complicated than this, however. First, although aluminum is a very active metal, it does not readily react with water directly. If it did, we could not use aluminum cans the way we do. The reason this does not ordinarily happen is that aluminum metal becomes coated by an oxide layer when it comes in contact with air. This layer is impervious and protects the metal from further oxidation. A strong base like potassium hydroxide will dissolve the oxide layer, exposing the metal and allowing the above reaction to take place.

Second, in the presence of strong base, the aluminum ion does not exist in isolation, but rather as a so-called complex, a central ion surrounded by several other molecules, called *ligands*. The complex formed in this case consists of a central Al^{3+} ion surrounded by 4 hydroxide (OH^-) ions and is appropriately named tetrahydroxoaluminate(III) ion. This complex has a net charge of 1^-. We can rewrite the chemical equation above reflecting the formation of the complex. In doing so, we can use hydroxide ions supplied by the potassium hydroxide solution. The result is the net ionic equation for the first step:

$$2Al(s) + 2OH^-(aq) + 6H_2O(l) \rightarrow 2Al(OH)_4^-(aq) + 3H_2(g) \tag{8.2}$$

Finally, if we wish to write a full molecular equation for this step, we include a potassium ion for each negative charge appearing on each side of the equation. The result is:

$$2Al(s) + 2KOH(aq) + 6H_2O(l) \rightarrow 2KAl(OH)_4(aq) + 3H_2(g) \tag{8.3}$$

Although K^+ is only a spectator ion in this step, in the overall synthesis, it is more than just a spectator. The final solid product incorporates potassium ions and the source of this potassium is the potassium hydroxide used.

Formation of potassium aluminum sulfate. The primary chemical reaction associated with formation of potassium aluminum sulfate change is the neutralization of the hydroxide ions within the complex ions produced in equation (8.2) (in ionic form) or equation (8.3) (in molecular form). Each $Al(OH)^{4-}$ ion requires 4 hydrogen ions, leading to the net ionic equation:

$$Al(OH)_4^-(aq) + 4H^+(aq) \rightarrow Al^{3+}(aq) + 4H_2O(l) \tag{8.4}$$

If this neutralization occurs in steps, then this reaction produces, in succession, $Al(OH)_3$, $Al(OH)_2^+$, $Al(OH)^{2+}$, and Al^{3+}. The ions are soluble in hot water, but the neutral aluminum hydroxide is not. This is why you may see the appearance of a precipitate, which dissolves in time.

The full molecular equation of this acid/base reaction is represented by rewriting equation (8.4) with the complex ion written as the KAl(OH)$_4$, and the hydrogen ions as sulfuric acid, H$_2$SO$_4$. Then the products would include all of the ions present in the final product in the correct proportions: K$^+$, Al^{3+}, and SO$_4^{2-}$, and can be written as KAl(SO$_4$)$_2$. Thus, this reaction can be regarded as the completion of the synthesis of potassium aluminum sulfate, although it still exists as separate ions in solution. The full molecular equation is

$$\text{KAl(OH)}_4\text{(aq)} + 2\text{H}_2\text{SO}_4 \text{ (l)} \rightarrow \text{KAl(SO}_4)_2\text{(aq)} + 4\text{H}_2\text{O(l)} \tag{8.5}$$

Notice that the sulfuric acid not only reacts with the hydroxide ligands, but also provides the sulfate, which is incorporated into the final product.

Crystallization and separation of alum. It is very common for an ionic compound to be soluble in hot water, but insoluble in cold water. Cooling a solution is a common way to remove such an ionic compound from solution. As discussed above, the ionic compound that crystallizes in this experiment is a hydrate, which includes 12 water molecules within each formula unit, i.e., it is a *dodecahydrate*. The net ionic equation representing the formation of the dodecahydrate, solid product is

$$\text{K}^+\text{(aq)} + \text{Al}^{3+}\text{(aq)} + 2\text{SO}_4^{2-}\text{(aq)} + 12\text{H}_2\text{O(l)} \rightarrow \text{KAl(SO}_4)_2 \bullet 12\text{H}_2\text{O(s)} \tag{8.6}$$

In full molecular form, equation (8.6) becomes

$$\text{KAl(SO}_4)_2\text{(aq)} + 12\text{H}_2\text{O(l)} \rightarrow \text{KAl(SO}_4)_2 \bullet 12\text{H}_2\text{O(s)} \tag{8.7}$$

This laboratory introduces students to the concepts of *limiting* and *excess reactants*, and *theoretical*, *actual*, and *percent yield*. If reactants are provided in amounts other than stoichiometric, one of the reactants will most certainly be consumed, leaving a reaction mixture of products and excess reactant. The reactant that is nearly completely consumed is called the limiting reactant, and thus, limits the amount of product formed.[1] "The amount of product that may be produced by a reaction under specified conditions, as calculated per the stoichiometry of an appropriate balanced chemical equation, is called the theoretical yield."[1] The actual yield or reaction yield, is the actual amount of product obtained in a chemical reaction. The extent to which a reaction's theoretical yield is achieved is expressed as a percentage, called percent yield, which is expressed mathematically as:

$$\% \text{ yield} = \frac{\text{g of product obtained}}{\text{g of product from theory}} \times 100 \tag{8.8}$$

The theoretical yield calculation assumes that only one reaction occurs and that the limiting reactant reacts completely. The actual yield is very often smaller than theoretical, i.e., the percent yield is less than 100, for several reasons: (1) reactions often do not go to completion rather they reach an equilibrated state where a combination of forward and reverse reactions produce a mixture containing both reactants and products, (2) side reactions may occur resulting in reactant(s) being converted to undesired products, (3) there is much potential for product loss as the desired product progresses through the separation and purification processes, and (4) the presence of impurities in the original reactants, which do not react to produce the desired product, serve to lower product yield. Generally speaking, yields above 80% are considered very good, while yields below 40% are considered poor.

The second part of this laboratory, i.e., Part B, is designed to verify if the synthesized product is indeed alum crystals. Students will analyze their product by determining: (1) the melting point, (2) the water of hydration, and (3) the percent sulfate of a sub-sample of the alum product. The melting point, i.e., the temperature at which a solid is converted to its liquid state, of an organic or low melting inorganic compound can help in the identification of a sample or to establish its purity. A pure compound will usually have a sharp and characteristic melting point, and possess a narrow melting range, e.g., 0.5 to 1.0°C. A sample that contains impurities, however, which is called a homogeneous mixture or solid solution, will melt at a lower temperature and over a wider range of temperatures, i.e., usually greater than 2°C. Students will use a Mel-Temp apparatus to obtain melting point ranges of their alum product, and then compare their experimental value to that of the literature value for pure alum. Generally, the greater the deviation from the literature value, the greater the amount of impurities, and the less pure their product.

The second verification test is to determine the water of hydration. Many inorganic salts exist as hydrates. Hydrates are compounds that have a definite number of water molecules loosely bound or trapped within the crystal lattice of the pure compound. The chemical formula of Alum, $KAl(SO_4)_2 \cdot 12H_2O$, indicates twelve waters of hydration, which classifies alum as a dodecahydrate, where "dodeca" is the prefix meaning for twelve. The twelve waters of hydration indicates that a mole of alum will contain twelve moles of water. By measuring the waters of hydration, students will gather additional evidence in support of or refuting the chemical formula of their synthesized product.

The final verification test student will conduct on a sub-sample of their synthesized product is to determine the mass percentage of sulfate. To accomplish this, students will dissolve a small amount of their product in distilled water, add excess 0.20 M $BaCl_2$ solution to completely precipitate sulfate ions, and then filter, dry, and mass the precipitate formed.

Crystals form much more slowly in the hot solution, and the formed crystals tend to be larger. The larger size makes them easier to filter, and because impurities are most often found on the surface of crystals, minimizing surface area by creating larger crystals will have the effect of reducing the amount of impurities.

The salient ionic equations associated with the dissolution of alum (8.9), total ionic (8.10), and net ionic reaction to form barium sulfate (8.11) are:

$$KAl(SO_4)_2•12H_2O(s) \rightarrow K^+(aq) + Al^{3+}(aq) + 2SO_4^{2-}(aq) + 12H_2O(l) \tag{8.9}$$

$$K^+(aq) + Al^{3+}(aq) + 2SO_4^{2-}(aq) + 12H_2O(l) + 2Ba^{2+}(aq) + 4Cl^-(aq) \rightarrow$$

$$K^+(aq) + Al^{3+}(aq) + 2BaSO_4(s) + 4Cl^-(aq) + 12H_2O(l) \tag{8.10}$$

$$SO_4^{2-}(aq) + Ba^{2+}(aq) \rightarrow BaSO_4(s) \tag{8.11}$$

The purpose of the experiment is to introduce some common laboratory techniques used in chemical synthesis and characterization, to demonstrate a synthesis of a useful substance called alum, apply the concepts of limiting reactant and reaction yield, and to perform several tests to verify the synthesis and purity of alum product. This laboratory also introduces students to the hydrate, which is a very important, and common chemical form of many inorganic salts.

Student Learning Outcomes: Upon completion of this laboratory experiment, students will be able to:

1. Synthesize alum.
2. Derive the full molecular equation for the synthesis of alum.
3. Calculate the percent yield of alum product.
4. Verify the presence and purity of alum product by determining the melting point, the water of hydration, and the percent sulfate of a sub-sample.

SAFETY NOTE: *WEAR EYE PROTECTION AT ALL TIMES! Potassium hydroxide, KOH, and sulfuric acid, H$_2$SO$_4$, are very corrosive. Both can cause severe burns if left in contact with the skin. Flush affected area with plenty of water; neutralize spills with sodium bicarbonate; Methanol is extremely flammable and its vapors are toxic. Keep methanol away from open flames and use in the fume hood; Bunsen burners can reach extreme temperatures, e.g., 900–1,600°C depending on fuel mixture; Use burners with caution; All long hair needs to be pinned back; Like all soluble barium compounds, barium nitrate is toxic by ingestion or inhalation. Treat barium with extreme caution!*

MATERIALS AND METHODS

Materials: hot plate, analytical balance, scissors, aluminum cans, 150- and 250-mL beakers, Whatman #1 (70 mm and 110 mm) and #42 (110 mm) filter paper, sandpaper with sanding cardboard, long-stem glass funnel, funnel support, ring stand, 0.20 M $BaCl_2$, 6 M HCl, 1.4 M potassium hydroxide (KOH), 9 M H_2SO_4, 0.1 M $AgNO_3$, conc. HNO_3, methanol, crushed ice, Büchner funnel, vacuum aspirator, rubber policeman with stir rod, 100-mL massing beaker, crucibles with lids, Bunsen burners, thermometer, Mel-Temp® Capillary Melting Point Apparatus with closed-end capillary tubes, and muffle furnace.

Methods

The experimental procedure for Part A of this experiment is adapted from "Synthesis of a chemical compound: Making alum from aluminum," from Chemistry in the Laboratory, James M. Postma, Julian L. Roberts, Jr., and J. Leland Hollenberg, New York: W.H. Freeman and Company, 2000.[2] The experimental procedure for Part B of this experiment is adapted from Advanced Chemistry with Vernier lab manual. The Analysis of Alum, 15B. Vernier Software & Technology Home Page. http://www.vernier.com/products/books/chem-a/#section4 (accessed May 2016).[3]

PART A. SYNTHESIS OF ALUM

Part A1. Oxidation of Aluminum

1. Cut a piece of aluminum about 5 cm square from an aluminum can. This aluminum has a label on the outside as well as an invisible plastic coating on the inside. Clean these off using a piece of sandpaper. A sanding cardboard is provided to catch the dust generated from the sanding process.

2. Weigh the aluminum piece and trim it with a scissors until its mass is approximately 0.5 g. Mass the aluminum accurately using the electronic analytical balance. This mass is very important, because aluminum is the limiting reactant and determines the maximum possible yield of the alum product.

3. Cut the aluminum into small pieces with a scissors and place in a 150-mL beaker. Smaller pieces have a greater surface area per unit mass and thus react at a faster rate. Large pieces may take some time to react completely.

4. While working in the fume hood, cautiously add 25 mL of 1.4 M KOH solution to the beaker containing the massed aluminum. Place the beaker on a hot plate and proceed to heat the beaker and its content at low heat. Warm the solution, but do not boil. With occasional stirring, all the aluminum should react in about 25–30 minutes.

5. While the aluminum is reacting, set up a long-stem glass funnel using a funnel support on a ring stand as depicted in Fig. 8.1D. Fold a piece of filter paper (Whatman® #1, 110 mm) into quarters, and place it in the funnel as demonstrated by your instructor (Fig. 8.1A–8.1C). Wet the filter paper with a small amount of distilled water. The stem of the funnel should empty into a 150-mL beaker (Fig. 8.1D).

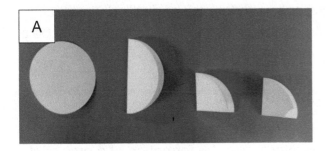

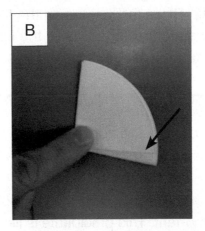

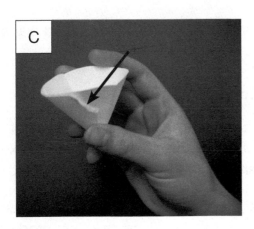

FIGURE 8.1   Folding filter paper and set-up for gravity filtration. Filter paper folding progression starting from left to right: (1) the unfolded paper, (2) paper folded in half and creased lightly, (3) paper folded in half again, i.e., in one-fourths or quarters, with the second folded edge extending about 10° from the right angle, and (4) folded paper with a small corner piece torn off (A); the quartered filter paper showing the second folded edge extending about 10° from the right angle as indicated by the black arrow (B); the folded filter paper in final form showing the small corner piece removed (black arrow) and paper properly opened and ready for placement in the funnel (C); the gravity filtration apparatus showing the ring stand, the funnel holder, the long-stem funnel with filter paper, collection beaker with stem of funnel touching the inside wall of the beaker, and the proper decantation technique. **Note**: when folding filter paper, always crease the folds lightly. Hard creases may cause small tears in the paper that result in leaking and thus, improper filtration. *Source: Frank Schindler*

Note: The reaction of the aluminum is complete when no aluminum remains in the beaker and bubbling has ceased. The solution may have a dirty "cloudiness" due to undissolved solids. This is due to impurities, which are to be removed by gravity filtration.

6. When the reaction is complete, pour the reaction mixture through the funnel using a stirring rod as illustrated in Fig. 8.1. Rinse the reaction beaker twice with 2 mL distilled water adding each rinse to the filter paper. Collect and save this liquid filtrate for Part A2. Rinse the residue on the filter paper with 2–3 mL of distilled water, joining this rinse to the filtrate. Save the filtrate for the next step. The filtrate should be a clear solution, which contains the desired product of the reaction.

Part A2. Formation of Potassium Aluminum Sulfate

1. Carefully, but quickly, add 10 mL of 9 M H_2SO_4 to the reaction filtrate from Part A1, step 6 while stirring. Record all observations, including the formation of a precipitate if any, and any changes in the temperature of the solution.

2. If there is a precipitate remaining at this point, heat the solution until it dissolves. This is very important. This precipitate is likely $Al(OH)_3(s)$ and **not** your desired product.

If time does not permit, cover your beaker with plastic wrap, label it, and place it in the tray for storage until next week.

Part A3. Crystallization and Separation of Alum

The desired product is now in solution in the beaker. Although it is soluble in hot water, its solubility decreases as the solution is cooled, i.e., the crystallization process is exothermic, therefore, reducing the heat favors shift toward crystallinity and away from dissolution.

1. Allow the 150-mL beaker containing the filtrate to cool. Fill a 600-mL beaker about half full of crushed ice. Place the 150-mL beaker containing the alum product in the ice bath for about 30 minutes, stirring frequently. As the solution cools, crystals of alum should begin to form. As the solution is cooling, set up a vacuum filtration apparatus with a Büchner funnel as demonstrated by your instructor and as depicted in Fig. 8.2.

2. Mass a clean, dry 100-mL beaker (tare mass) and a (Whatman® #1, 70 mm) filter paper (filter paper mass) using the top-loading balance. The purpose of this beaker is to collect the final solid alum product. Record both masses in your notebook.

3. When the crystallization is complete, stir **carefully** with a thermometer, and record the temperature when the reading stabilizes. The temperature should be 6°C or less.

4. Place the filter paper in the Büchner funnel, turn on the house vacuum, and proceed to pour ice water through the Büchner funnel. Cooling the vacuum filtration apparatus minimizes the potential redissolution of alum due to an abrupt temperature increase.

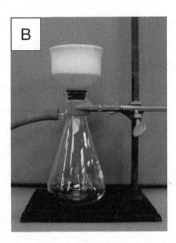

FIGURE 8.2 Top view of vacuum filtration apparatus with Büchner funnel and seal, 70 mm filter paper, vacuum flask, and vacuum hose (A); Profile of vacuum filtration apparatus showing ring stand and clamp (B). The clamp is necessary to hold the flask securely. *Source: Frank Schindler*

5. Remove the beaker containing the alum from the ice bath, and stir the contents of the beaker with a stirring rod to loosen all of the crystals. Transfer all of the crystals to the Büchner funnel. A rubber policeman may be useful in this process. Add three 10-mL portions of methanol in succession to wash the excess sulfuric acid out of the crystals. Continue running the vacuum for another 10 to 15 minutes. The air that is drawn through the alum crystals aid in drying the crystals.

6. Carefully transfer the dried alum crystals and filter paper to the massed beaker. Remass the beaker containing the dried alum crystals and filter paper (gross mass). To obtain the mass of alum product only, subtract the filter paper mass plus tare mass from the gross mass.

7. Slowly add sodium hydrogen carbonate, NaHCO$_3$ (baking soda), to the filter flask to neutralize the excess acid. Continue to add baking soda in small amounts until the bubbling or effervescence subsides.

8. Rinse the neutralized solution in the filter flask down the drain, and then clean the flask and your work area.

PART B. VERIFICATION OF ALUM

Part B1. Melting Point Determination

1. Use a mortar and pestle to pulverize about 0.5 g of dry alum and place it in a small pile on a watch glass. Push the open end of a capillary tube into the pile of the alum powder until a small amount of product is forced into the tube end (about 1 to 2 mm is more than enough).

2. Invert the capillary tube and drop it, closed end down, down a long-stem funnel. Doing this will force and pack your small amount of sample down into the bottom of

the tube. You may have to repeat this packing several times to ensure all sample is adequately packed into the bottom.

3. Make sure the Mel-Temp® Capillary Melting Point Apparatus (Fig. 8.3) is near room temperature. Use a fan or lab air to aid in cooling apparatus if needed. Turn the instrument on, and then insert the tube into one of three small slots located in the instrument's mantle, NOT in the large hole where the thermometer goes. Look through the viewfinder at the front of the instrument and locate your sample. Monitor your sample with your eye about 6 inches from viewfinder.

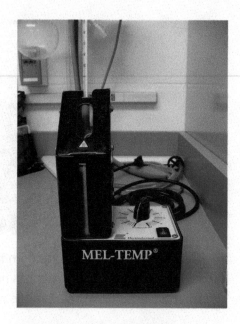

FIGURE 8.3   Mel-Temp® Capillary Melting Point Apparatus. *Source: Frank Schindler*

4. Perform an initial melting point determination that provides a rapid, but crude estimation of the melting point. Begin heating the sample rapidly (set power level to 5 or higher) and then record the temperature when the product melts. Cool the instrument.

5. Having a rough estimate of the melting point, perform a more accurate determination by preparing a fresh sample as outlined in step 1, above, setting the power level to 5, and then heating the sample until the temperature is about 20°C below the expected melting point.

6. At this point, turn the dial down to the setting indicated by the "Power Levels" located on the Mel-Temp Heating Curve located at the instrument workstation. You will get the most accurate reading by slowing down the rate of heating as the expected melting point temperature is approached.

7. Record two temperatures: (1) the temperature at which your sample begins to melt, and (2) the temperature at which the last portion of solid melts completely. The melting point of your product should be recorded in your notebook as a range, not a discrete value.

Part B2. Water of Hydration

1. Start with a clean, crack-free crucible and crucible lid. Place the crucible on a wire triangle setting atop a metal ring attached to a ring stand as depicted in Fig. 8.4. Place the crucible lid slightly ajar on the crucible to allow water vapor to escape.

2. Light and adjust the Bunsen burner to a nonluminous flame. Heat the crucible gently for several minutes to drive off most water, and then vigorously for several minutes to dry the crucible more completely.

3. Turn off the burner and allow the crucible and lid to cool for about 2 minutes. Using crucible tongs, transfer the crucible and lid to a desiccator and allow to cool to near room temperature. When placing very hot objects in a desiccator, the desiccator lid should be slid open just a very small amount to allow for pressure equalization due to air expansion. Close the desiccator completely after several minutes.

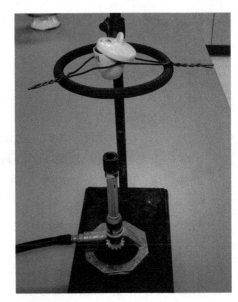

FIGURE 8.4 Crucible and hydrate dehydration set-up.
Source: Frank Schindler

4. Once cooled, transfer the crucible with lid to the analytical balance and record a tare mass. Make sure to always use tongs and not your hands, because the moisture and/or oil from your fingers will add to the mass and effect your results. Also, never mass anything that is not room temperature.

5. Repeat the drying, cooling, and massing procedure as outlined in steps 2–4 until the mass of crucible and lid agrees to within 0.03 g of the initial tare mass. Once this constant mass has been obtained, proceed to the next step.

6. Place about 1 g of your alum crystals in the dried crucible, and then mass the crucible plus lid plus alum on the analytical balance. Record this mass in your notebook as "gross hydrate mass." Again, make sure not to touch the crucible with your bare hands.

7. Using your tongs, set the crucible with the lid slightly ajar on the wire triangle. Light the Bunsen burner and gently heat the crucible with lid and hydrate until you can no longer see vapor escaping from the crucible. It is important that the vapor does not carry any alum with it. After the vapor is gone, heat the crucible more strongly for five minutes. DO NOT allow the crucibles to become red-hot! Discontinue heating if white smoke appears or you smell a pungent, irritating odor. The odor is a symptom of SO$_4^{2-}$ decomposing to SO$_2$(g).

8. Turn off the burner and cool the crucible, lid, and alum according to the procedures outlined in step 3, above. Once cooled, transfer the crucible with lid and alum to the analytical balance and record the "gross anhydrous mass."

9. Repeat the heating, cooling, and massing procedures until the mass of crucible, lid, and anhydrous agrees to within 0.05 g of the initial mass. The procedure is complete once a constant mass has been achieved.

10. Once a final, constant mass has been recorded in your notebook, transfer the anhydrous product to the appropriately labeled waste container located in the fume hood.

Part B3. Percent Sulfate in Alum by Gravimetric Analysis

1. Obtain a clean crucible with lid and record its identification in your notebook. Place the crucible and lid in the muffle furnace at approximately 600°C for 1 hour. Make sure the lid is set on top of the crucible and slightly ajar. After heating, use your tongs to remove the crucible and place them in a desiccator for at least 30 minutes. Once the crucibles have cooled to room temperature, mass them with lid and record this mass in your notebook. Repeat this procedure until successive massings agree to within 0.5 mg. This is your "tare mass of crucible plus lid." Perform this step while conducting steps 2 through 11. Save the crucible and lid for step 11, below.

2. Zero the analytical balance, and then mass accurately a creased sheet of glazed massing paper plus about 0.5 g of your alum sample ("mass of glazed paper plus alum"). *To "mass accurately" means to obtain a mass close to the desired mass, and then record the mass to at least three or four decimal places. For example, if a glazed massing paper when placed on a balance weighs 0.3456 g, and you want about 0.5 g of sample, you would proceed to add sample to the paper until the mass is about 0.85 g. You close the balance door and record the mass accurately. The actual amount is not important. What is important is that you know what the actual amount is very accurately, since this is the mass needed in your calculations.* Quantitatively transfer the alum to a 250-mL beaker and then mass the glazed paper after sample transfer ("mass of glazed paper after transfer") to obtain, by difference, the mass of alum dissolved.

3. Add about 50 mL of distilled water followed by ca. 20 drops of 6 *M* HCl to the 250-mL beaker containing the alum. Stir the acidified alum solution with stir rod to dissolve the sample. Do not remove stir rod.

4. Calculate the volume of 0.20 *M* $BaCl_2$ solution needed to completely precipitate the sulfate ions in the beaker of alum solution using the stoichiometric relationships in equations (8.9–8.11). For example, use your mass of alum transferred to the 250-mL beaker and perform the following calculation:

$$\text{L of BaCl}_2 = (\text{Alum, g})\left(\frac{1 \text{ mol Alum}}{474.22 \text{ g Alum}}\right)\left(\frac{2 \text{ mol SO}_4^{2-}}{1 \text{ mol Alum}}\right)\left(\frac{1 \text{ mol Ba}^{2+}}{1 \text{ mol SO}_4^{2-}}\right)$$

$$\left(\frac{1 \text{ L}}{0.20 \text{ mol Ba}^{2+}}\right) \tag{8.12}$$

Measure out twice the calculated volume in a clean graduated cylinder. **CAUTION: Handle the $BaCl_2$ solution with care, because it is toxic. Wipe up any spills and wash your hands thoroughly.** Pour the measured $BaCl_2$ solution into a small beaker and heat it to ca. 60°C. A temperature of 60°C is about an object temperature that most people can hold on to continuously.

5. Prepare the precipitate by placing a watch glass over the beaker containing the alum solution and stir rod, placing the beaker on a hot plate, and then heating the solution

to near boiling, i.e., ca. 90°C. With continued heating below the boiling point and constant stirring, slowly add (over a 10-minute period) small portions of the heated 0.20 M BaCl$_2$ solution to the alum solution. You should observe the formation of the sparingly soluble BaSO$_4$(s) precipitate. Once all 0.20 M BaCl$_2$ solution has been added, continue heating and stirring occasionally for about 60–75 minutes. This process, called digestion, aids in the formation of larger, purer crystals of barium sulfate.

6. Remove the beaker from the hot plate and allow the BaSO$_4$(s) crystals to settle out of solution.

   If time does not permit, cover your beaker with plastic wrap, label it, and place it in the tray for storage until next week.

7. Test the clear supernatant solution for reaction completeness by adding a few drops of the 0.20 M BaCl$_2$ solution. If the solution remains clear, i.e., no cloudiness, at the point of entry, the precipitation is complete and filtration can proceed. If cloudiness forms as the drops enter the solution, an additional volume of 0.20 M BaCl$_2$ solution must be added and the sample digested further.

8. With the precipitated solution at approximately 60°C, decant the clear supernatant solution through an ashless filter paper (Whatman #42, 110 mm) that has been folded and placed in a gravity filtration funnel as depicted in Fig. 8.1D. Collect the filtrate in a clean beaker in the event some crystals pass through the filter and a second filtration is needed.

9. Wash the BaSO$_4$(s) crystals remaining in the beaker with a 10 mL aliquot of 60°C distilled water, and then decant through filter. Do this washing/decantation step several times. At the last decantation, transfer the crystals to the filter with warm water. Do not allow the liquid level to reach above the top of the filter paper.

10. Loosen all crystals adhering to the walls of the beaker and stirring rod with a rubber policeman and wash into filter. Check the filtrate for particles by gently swirling the beaker and looking for a collection of particles in the center of beaker. If no collection exists, the filtrate can be discarded in the proper waste container. If particles do collect, the filtrate needs to be digested again and filtered through a fresh filter. Both filters need to be saved for combustion.

11. Wash the crystals on the filter paper by adding warm water to within an eighth of an inch from the top of the funnel and then allow it to drain completely. Filling the funnel to within an eighth of an inch from the top creates a column of water, which accelerates the filtration by gravity. Perform this washing step 3 additional times. Use a clean beaker to collect the fourth washing. When completely drained, check the washing for the presence of chloride by adding 2 drops of concentrated HNO$_3$ and several drops of 0.1 M AgNO$_3$. A white precipitate of AgCl(s) will appear if the washing in not complete. If the test is positive, perform another washing. Continue washing the crystals until the Cl$^-$ test is negative. Run a Cl$^-$ test on distilled water for comparative purposes.

12. <u>Carefully</u> remove the filter paper from the funnel and carefully fold the paper containing the $BaSO_4$ crystals into a small package that is able to fit into the dried and tared crucible. In the fume hood, place the crucible with filter on a ring stand equipped with a clay triangle. Commence heating the crucible without lid at low heat to dry the filter and contents. Once the filter is dry, heat the crucible more vigorously to start the charring process. The paper should turn brown and eventfully black (charred) without bursting into flames. Have your lid ready on the clay triangle and your tongs in-hand in case the paper flares up. If it does, douse the flames with the crucible lid. Continue heating the crucible until paper is well charred. It may be necessary to add ammonium nitrate (NH_4NO_3) to the paper to effect complete charring. The ammonium nitrate undergoes simultaneous thermal dissociation to ammonia and nitric acid vapor and decomposition to nitrous oxide and water during the charring process.

13. Using crucible tongs, transfer the crucible to the muffle furnace (600°C) first without the lid and check for flare-up. If the paper begins to burn brightly and flames up when placing the crucible in the furnace, remove the crucible and then slowly reinsert it into the muffle furnace. When the risk of flare up subsides, place the crucible lid ajar and heat the crucible for 1 hour. The furnace serves to combust the charred filter paper, converting it to CO_2 gas. Upon complete combustion, only white $BaSO_4$ should remain in the crucible.

14. After heating crucible in the muffle furnace for the allotted time, remove the crucible with lid and allow it to cool in air for several minutes, and then place it in a desiccator to cool. When the crucible reaches approximately room temperature, mass it on the analytical balance (±0.0001 g). This is your "mass of crucible plus lid plus $BaSO_4$(s) crystals."

15. After massing your crucible, dump its contents into the appropriately labeled container located in the fume hood.

Calculations

1. Combine equations (8.3), (8.5), and (8.7) to find the overall molecular equation for the synthesis of alum. Notice that you will need to include equations (8.5) and (8.7) multiplied by a factor of 2 to cancel the intermediate formed in equation (8.3).

2. Use the full molecular equation for the synthesis along with the formula mass of alum to calculate a *theoretical yield* of alum assuming that the aluminum metal is the limiting reactant.

3. From your data, find the net mass of alum produced by subtracting the "filter paper mass" plus "tare mass" from the "gross mass" of Part A3. This is the actual yield. Determine the *percentage yield* in the synthesis by comparing the actual yield to the theoretical yield by using equation (8.8).

4. Determine the water of hydration (Part B2) for your alum product by performing the following calculations:

   a. Determine the mass of the sample hydrate by subtracting the "tare mass" of the crucible from the "gross hydrate mass" of Part B2:

$$\text{Mass of hydrate (g)} = (\text{gross hydrate mass, g}) - (\text{tare mass, g}) \qquad (8.13)$$

   b. Determine the mass of water lost by subtracting the "gross anhydrous mass" from the "gross hydrate mass" of Part B2:

$$\text{Mass of water (g)} = (\text{gross hydrate mass, g}) - (\text{gross anhydrous mass, (g)} \qquad (8.14)$$

   c. Determine the mole of water lost by dividing the mass of water (8.14) by the molar mass of water:

$$\text{mol of H}_2\text{O} = \frac{\text{mass of H}_2\text{O, g}}{\text{molar mass of H}_2\text{O, g mol}^{-1}} \qquad (8.15)$$

   d. Determine the mass of anhydrous by subtracting the "tare mass" of the crucible from the "gross anhydrous mass" of Part B2:

$$\text{Mass of anhydrous (g)} = (\text{gross anhydrous mass, g}) - (\text{tare mass, g}) \qquad (8.16)$$

   e. Determine the mole of anhydrous by dividing the mass of anhydrous (8.16) by the molar mass of anhydrous:

$$\text{mol of anhydrous} = \frac{\text{mass of anhydrous, g}}{\text{molar mass of anhydrous, g mol}^{-1}} \qquad (8.17)$$

   f. The formula of the alum hydrate is determined by calculating the ratio of the moles of water to the moles of anhydrous:

$$\text{mole ratio} = \frac{\text{mol H}_2\text{O}}{\text{mol anhydrous}} \qquad (8.18)$$

5. Determine the percentage sulfate in alum (Part B3) by performing the following calculations:

   a. Determine the "mass of alum reacted" by subtracting the "mass of glazed paper after transfer" from the "mass of glazed paper plus alum" before transfer to the 250-mL beaker:

$$\text{Mass of alum reacted (g)} = (\text{mass of glazed paper plus alum, g}) - (\text{mass of glazed paper after transfer, g}) \qquad (8.19)$$

b. Determine the mass of $BaSO_4(s)$ crystals formed by subtracting the "tare mass of crucible plus lid" from the "mass of crucible plus lid plus $BaSO_4(s)$ crystals" of Part B3:

Mass $BaSO_4(s)$ crystals formed (g) = (mass of crucible plus lid plus $BaSO_4(s)$ crystals, g) − (tare mass of crucible plus lid, g)   (8.20)

c. Determine the mass of SO_4^{2-} from the mass of $BaSO_4(s)$ crystals formed:

$$\text{mass of } SO_4^{2-} = (\text{mass of } BaSO_4(s))\left(\frac{96.063 \text{ g } SO_4^{2-}}{233.40 \text{ g } BaSO_4(s)}\right)$$ (8.21)

d. Determine the percent SO_4^{2-} by dividing the mass of SO_4^{2-} by the mass of alum reacted:

$$\text{percent } SO_4^{2-} (m/m) = \left(\frac{\text{mass of } SO_4^{2-}, \text{ g}}{\text{mass of Alum reacted, g}}\right)(100)$$ (8.22)

e. Compare your percentage to the actual percent sulfate by mass in alum.

Results

Summarize your results by tabulating: (1) the molecular and net ionic equations for the synthesis of alum, (2) the theoretical yield, (3) your percent yield, (4) the melting point range of your alum product and the literature value, (5) the water of hydration, and thus the mole ratio of water to anhydrous form and your experimentally determined chemical formula of the alum hydrate, (6) the percentage by mass of sulfate of your alum product.

Discussion/Conclusions

In your discussion, summarize the entire synthesis starting with the addition of each reactant, the progression through to formation of intermediates and then the final product. For example: "The KOH was added in step 1 as 25 mL of a 1.4 M solution to the aluminum metal which caused . . ." Interpret your results and relate them to the objectives of the experiment. Discuss relationships, generalizations, shortcomings, and difficulties of the experiment. Focus your discussion on the meaning of your findings, not to recapitulate them. How does your yield of alum compare to the theoretical yield? What are some possible explanations for any deviation from the expected?

In addition, you should discuss the verification tests performed on a sub-sample of your alum product. Based on the melting point range, the mole ratio of water to anhydrous, and the percent sulfate, is your product likely alum? Is your product pure or does it contain impurities?

Your conclusions should explicitly state your alum amount and percent yield. Speculate on the unaccounted alum if you obtained less than 100% yield. Also, include the melting point range, your experimentally determined chemical formula of the alum hydrate, and the percent sulfate. You should conclude the identity of your synthesized product based on the empirical evidence.

REFERENCES

1. Flowers, P.; Theopold, K.; Langley, R.; Robinson, W. *Chemistry*, OpenStax College. 2019. (https://openstax.org/details/books/chemistry-2e).

2. Postma, J. M.; Roberts, J. L., Jr.; Hollenberg, J. L. *Chemistry in the Laboratory*. Synthesis of a chemical compound: Making alum from aluminum. W.H. Freeman and Company: New York, 2000.

3. Vernier Software & Technology, *Advanced Chemistry with Vernier lab manual*. The Analysis of Alum, 15B. Vernier Software & Technology Home Page. http://www.vernier.com/products/books/chem-a/#section4 (accessed May 2016).

EXPERIMENT 9

Determining the Molar Volume of Select Gases

INTRODUCTION

In the gas phase, matter is considerably less dense than in the liquid or solid phases. Alternatively, the volume occupied by a gas is very large compared to the same amount of liquid or solid. Gases are also very compressible, meaning that their volumes can be readily changed by the application of pressure or by a change in temperature. Under the proper conditions, many substances display very simple universal relationships among these

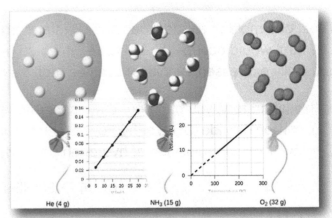

Source line: Download for free at https://openstax. org/details/books/chemistry.

properties. Collectively, these relationships are called gas laws. For example, there is a simple relationship between volume and pressure called Boyle's Law: "the volume of a given amount of gas held at constant temperature is inversely proportional to the pressure under which it is measured."[1] Our current understanding of the direct proportionality that exists between gas volume and temperature at constant pressure and quantity, and gas pressure and temperature at constant volume and quantity, are universally accepted, credited to Jacques Charles and Joseph Louis Gay-Lussac, and are known as Charles' and Gay-Lussac's laws, respectively.

In this experiment, students will attempt to confirm one of the universal gas laws. In 1811, Amedeo Avogadro postulated, "For a confined gas, the volume (V) and the number of moles (n) are directly proportional if the pressure and temperature both remain constant."[1]

This relationship is known as Avogadro's Law and the mathematical equivalence of this statement is

$$\frac{V_1}{n_1} = \frac{V_2}{n_2} \tag{9.1}$$

Therefore, Avogadro's Law implies that the volumes occupied by one mole of any gas should be the same provided the volumes are measured under the same temperature and pressure conditions.

The volume of each gas produced will be measured by the water displacement method. The moles of each gas will be determined by the amount of limiting reactant used and the stoichiometric relationship of the balanced molecular equation. By dividing the volume of gas by the number of moles, you obtain a quantity called the *molar volume*, V_m,

$$V_m = \frac{\text{liters of gas, L}}{\text{moles of gas, } n} \tag{9.2}$$

Thus, one mole of an ideal gas at STP (standard temperature of 273.15 K and pressure of 1 atm) would occupy 22.414 L, i.e., it would have a V_m equal to 22.414 L mol^{-1}, which is usually expressed in units of L, since mol^{-1} is implied.

In this laboratory, you carry out three separate reactions, each producing either oxygen (O_2), carbon dioxide (CO_2), or hydrogen (H_2) gas. In part 1 of the experiment, you produce $O_2(g)$ by the decomposition of hydrogen peroxide:

$$H_2O_2(l) \rightarrow H_2O(l) + \tfrac{1}{2}O_2(g) \tag{9.3}$$

The liquid reactant is 3% hydrogen peroxide solution, while the solid reactant is potassium iodide, KI. The KI serves as a catalyst in the decomposition of $H_2O_2(l)$, and is not really a reactant, since it is not consumed in the process.

In Part 2 of this experiment, $CO_2(g)$ will be produced by the reaction of sodium bicarbonate with hydrochloric acid:

$$NaHCO_3(s) + HCl(aq) \rightarrow NaCl(aq) + H_2O(l) + CO_2(g) \tag{9.4}$$

The liquid reactant is 20 mL of a 3 M hydrochloric acid solution and the solid reactant is 1 g of sodium bicarbonate.

Hydrogen gas will be produced in Part 3 by the reaction of magnesium metal with hydrochloric acid:

$$Mg(s) + 2HCl\,(aq) \rightarrow MgCl_2(aq) + H_2(g) \tag{9.5}$$

The liquid reactant is 20 mL of a 3 M hydrochloric acid solution and the solid reactant is 0.3 g of magnesium metal.

To determine the volume of gas produced from a chemical reaction, a basic water displacement apparatus is used (Fig. 9.1). Each reaction consists of a liquid reactant and a solid reactant. The liquid is placed in the reaction flask [Fig. 9.1(1)] and the solid in a small vial or test tube inside the flask so that it will not come in contact with the liquid when the apparatus is shaken. When the liquid and solid reactants react, gas is produced and is forced from the reaction flask into the displacement flask [Fig. 9.1(2)] containing a large volume of water. The gas pushes water from this displacement flask through rubber tubing into a collection beaker [Fig. 9.1(3)]. When the reaction is complete, the pressure inside the displacement apparatus is manually equalized with the atmospheric pressure. Consequently, the total pressure inside the displacement flask is, according to Dalton's Law of Partial Pressures, equal to the sum of the partial pressures of the gas and water vapor:

$$P_{laboratory} = P_{H_2O} + P_{gas} \tag{9.6}$$

where $P_{laboratory}$ is the corrected atmospheric pressure obtained from a barometric reading, P_{gas} is the partial pressure of the evolved gas and P_{H_2O} is the vapor pressure of water, which can be obtained from the CRC Handbook of Chemistry and Physics located in the laboratory.

The atmospheric pressures reported from weather stations and airports are typically corrected to sea level, and do not correctly represent the pressure exerted under local conditions or in the laboratory. Consequently, the laboratory pressure will be estimated using the equation:

$$P_{laboratory} = P_{sea\ level}\, e^{\frac{-elevation}{(T)(29.263)}} \tag{9.7}$$

where elevation is meters above sea level in Marshall, MN and is 360 meters, $P_{sea\ level}$ is the barometric pressure from the local weather service, and T is the room temperature in kelvin.

FIGURE 9.1 Apparatus for determining the molar volume of a gas (A). Inset (B) depicts an exploded view of the solid reactant vessel when placed in the 250-mL reaction flask; image shows the 250-mL reaction flask (1); the 500-mL displacement flask (2), and the 600-mL collection beaker (3). *Source: Frank Schindler*

By measuring the volume of water displaced by the gas sample, you measure the volume of the gas itself at the temperature inside the lab apparatus, and under a pressure equal to the atmospheric pressure in the lab. You will need to convert this volume under lab conditions to volume at STP. Assuming that Boyle's and Charles' laws apply, the volume of collected gas at STP, V_2, is calculated using the combined gas law as:

$$V_2 = \frac{V_1 P_1 T_2}{T_1 P_2} \qquad (9.8)$$

where V_1 is the measured volume of gas, i.e., the volume of displaced water, P_1 is the partial pressure of evolved gas or P_{gas} from equation (9.6), T_2 is standard temperature of 273.15 K, T_1 is measured experimental temperature in K, and P_2 is the standard pressure of 1 atm.

Before you can convert the volume of gas under laboratory conditions to its volume at STP, you will need to correct the gas pressure in the apparatus, $P_{laboratory}$, to that of just the evolved gas, P_{gas}, using equation (9.6). That is, the evolved gas is confined in the two flasks with water, so part of the pressure inside the apparatus is the pressure of water vapor. To make the necessary correction, subtract the vapor pressure of water at the experimental temperature (CRC Handbook) from the total pressure of the gas. The total pressure is equal to the corrected barometric pressure, $P_{laboratory}$, determined from (9.7).

The objectives of this experiment are to compute and compare the molar volumes of three different gases. You will do so by measuring the volume of water displaced as a result of gas generation from various reactions, expressing the gas volume at STP, calculating moles of gas by either mass difference or stoichiometric relationships, and then calculating their molar volumes.

Student Learning Outcomes: Upon completion of this laboratory experiment, students will be able to:

1. Determine the molar volume of O_2, CO_2, and H_2 using water displacement.
2. Relate experimental findings to Avogadro's Law.

SAFETY NOTE: *WEAR EYE PROTECTION AT ALL TIMES! Hydrochloric acid, HCl, is very corrosive, and can cause severe burns if left in contact with the skin. Flush affected area with plenty of water; neutralize spills with sodium bicarbonate; discard neutralized solutions down drain; Do not touch the magnesium metal with your hands. Always use forceps when handling metals; H_2 is produced in Part 3, and is potentially explosive in the presence of O_2; do not use open flames.*

MATERIALS AND METHODS

Materials: A 250 mL and 500 mL Erlenmeyer Flask, one one-hole rubber stopper to fit 250 mL Erlenmeyer Flask, one two-hole rubber stopper for 500 mL Erlenmeyer Flask, 6–8 cm lengths 6-mm glass tubing, 30 cm length of 6-mm OD glass tubing with 90° bend 8 cm from one end, disposal transfer pipets, 3/16 inch-ID rubber tubing, pinch clamp, thermometer, 500-mL graduated cylinder, one 10 mL and one 50- or 100-mL graduated cylinder, 3% hydrogen peroxide solution, potassium iodide (KI), 3 M hydrochloric acid (HCl) solution, sodium bicarbonate ($NaHCO_3$), magnesium metal.

Methods

The experimental procedure of this experiment is adapted from "The Molar Volume of Dioxygen and Other Gases," from Chemistry in the Laboratory, James M. Postma, Julian L. Roberts, Jr., and J. Leland Hollenberg, New York: W.H. Freeman and Company, 2000.[2]

You will need to record the data as outlined in Table 9.1 for each part of this laboratory experiment.

The following is a step-by-step procedure for carrying out any of the reactions. The stopper, tube, and test clamp assemblies are already prepared for you. Refer to Fig. 9.1 to see how everything fits together. All calculations need to be computed in the "Calculation" section of your notebook. Likewise, all results need to be tabulated in the "results" section of your notebook.

TABLE 9.1   Data needed to determine the molar volume of gases.

Data	unit
Laboratory pressure, $P_{laboratory}$	atm
Volume of H_2O_2 used (Part 1 only):	mL
Mass of 5.0 mL of H_2O_2 (Part 1 only):	g
Temperature of gas in reaction flask:	°C
Temperature of gas in displacement flask:	°C
Volume of gas collected:	mL
Water vapor pressure at experimental temperature:	torr

Part 1. Molar Volume of Oxygen (O₂) Gas

1. Record the barometric pressure, $P_{sea\ level}$, provided. This pressure must be corrected to represent the pressure exerted under laboratory conditions, i.e., $P_{laboratory}$, to use for Parts 1, 2, and 3.

2. Cut the bulb end of a disposable transfer pipet (about 1 cm in length) (see Fig. 9.2) and use this to hold the solid reactant, KI. This is referred to as the solid reactant vessel. The solid reactant vessel in this form facilitates reactant mixing and eliminates wedging the solid reactant container within the reaction flask.

3. Mass a 10.0-mL graduated cylinder marked as "TC," which means "to contain," on the analytical balance. Record this as the tare mass.

4. Measure exactly 5.0 mL of a 3% hydrogen peroxide solution in the 10.0 mL cylinder and then mass the cylinder plus 5.0 mL hydrogen peroxide on the analytical balance (gross mass). This will be used to determine the density of the 3% hydrogen peroxide solution in Part 1 of the calculations section, below.

5. Using a 50.0 mL graduated cylinder, measure 30.0 mL of a 3% hydrogen peroxide solution, and add it to the 250-mL reaction flask (Fig. 9.1).

6. Add approximately 0.5 g of potassium iodide, KI, to the solid reactant vessel.

7. Using forceps, carefully place the solid reactant vessel within the reaction flask. The solid-reactant vessel should float without a mixing of reactants. Be careful not to disturb the reaction vessel once the solid reactant container has been placed in the reaction flask; you do not want premature mixing of reactants. As an alternate method, place the one-hole rubber stopper with short glass tube on the reaction flask containing the hydrogen peroxide and KI reactant vessel. Accurately mass the reaction flask with stopper, tube, and reactant vessel on an analytical balance. Be sure not to exceed the mass capacity of the balance.

8. Fill the 500 mL displacement flask almost completely with water as shown in Fig. 9.1.

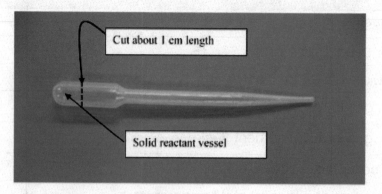

FIGURE 9.2   Cut the bulb end of a disposal transfer pipet to use as a solid-reactant vessel.
Source: Frank Schindler

9. Place the two-hole stopper with the long glass tube into the 500 mL displacement flask and the other end of the rubber tube into the collection beaker as shown in Fig. 9.1. Leave the pinch clamp open and do not yet seal the reaction flask with the other stopper. The glass tube on the large flask should reach almost to the bottom.

10. Add some water (the amount is not critical) to the collection beaker. Approximately one fourth full is convenient.

11. Get a siphon started between the displacement flask and the collection beaker by blowing into the (yet unattached) tube on the one-hole stopper (use a pipet bulb NOT your mouth). Blow hard enough to force all the air out of the tube between the displacement flask and the collection beaker. When the siphon is started, you should be able to move water back and forth between the displacement flask and the collection beaker simply by raising and lowering the collection beaker.

12. Raise the collection beaker so that the displacement flask is filled nearly to the top with water.

13. Equalize pressure by positioning the collection beaker so its water level is the same as that in the displacement flask. While holding this position, place the one-hole stopper on the reaction flask and seal tightly.

14. Test the apparatus for leaks by raising the collection beaker as high as possible without removing the tubing from the beaker. The water level in the displacement flask should move some, but then stop and remain fixed. If the water level continues to change, a leak is present and must be fixed before continuing.

15. Again equalize the pressures by positioning the collection beaker so its water level is the same as that in the displacement flask. While holding this position, have your partner close the pinch clamp. Discard all of the water in the collection beaker.

16. Place the tube back in the beaker and then open the pinch clamp. When you do, you may see a small amout of water flow from the flask to the collection beaker. This is normal and will not lead to errors in the results. (Do not discard this water.)

17. Shake the reaction flask to allow the solid and liquid to mix. As gas is produced, you should see water forced from the displacement flask to the collection beaker. Continuously swirl the reaction flask to ensure near completion of the reaction. If all of the water is forced out of the displacement flask, you will need to redo the experiment with smaller amounts. Make sure the transfer tube remains below the surface of the water in the collection beaker during gas generation.

18. After the reaction is complete, i.e., about 20 to 30 minutes, with the stoppers on and the flasks still tightly sealed, adjust the heights of the collection beaker and the displacement flask so that the water levels are equal. This assures that the pressure is the same throughout the apparatus and is equal to the pressure of the atmosphere. Water may flow between the displacement flask and the collection beaker as you adjust the levels.

19. With the water levels equalized, close the pinch clamp to stop the siphon action.

20. Loosen the stopper of the reaction flask and insert a thermometer into the gas. Measure the temperature and record the value in your notebook (allow at least 1 minute for temperature to stabilize before reading the thermometer). Take the same temperature measurement for the displacement flask. At this point and as part of the alternate method, disconnect the latex tubing from the one-hole stopper of the reaction vessel and accurately mass the reaction flask with stopper, glass tube, and reactant vessel on an analytical balance. Be sure not to exceed the mass capacity of the balance.

21. Measure the volume of the water contained in the collection beaker with a graduated cylinder. This represents the volume of gas produced in the reaction.

22. Pour the contents of the reaction flask into the recovered chemical container located in the fume hood. Clean the flask and proceed to Part 2. Retain the solid reactant vessel for Part 2.

Part 2. Molar Volume of Carbon Dioxide (CO_2) Gas

1. Using a graduated cylinder, measure 20 mL of the 3 M hydrochloric acid solution and add it to the 250 mL reaction flask (Fig. 9.1).

2. Mass the solid reactant vessel on the analytical balance, and record its tare mass in your notebook. Add approximately 1.0 g of sodium bicarbonate to the solid reactant vessel and record an accurate gross mass. The difference between these two masses equals the mass of sodium bicarbonate reacted. The sodium bicarbonate needs to be accurately massed, because the moles of CO_2 produced in this acid/base neutralization reaction is determined by stoichiometric relationship of equation (9.4).

3. Use a forceps to carefully place the solid reactant vessel within the reaction flask. The solid-reactant receiving vessel should float without a mixing of reactants. Be careful not to disturb the reaction vessel once the solid reactant container has been placed in the reaction flask; you do not want premature mixing of reactants. Do not seal it yet.

4. Prepare your displacement flasks and collect gas as outlined in steps 8–21 of Part 1, above.

5. When the experiment is complete, add small increments of baking soda to the reaction flask to neutralize any excess acid present. When the content ceases to effervesce (or fizz), discard the content down the drain and flush.

6. If this is the last part performed, disassemble the apparatus and clean up.

Part 3. Molar Volume of Hydrogen (H_2) Gas

1. Using a graduated cylinder, measure 20 mL of the 3 M hydrochloric acid solution and add it to the 250 mL reaction flask (Fig. 9.1).

2. Mass the solid reactant vessel on the analytical balance, and record its tare mass in your notebook. Add approximately 0.3 g of magnesium metal to the solid reactant vessel and record an accurate gross mass. The difference between these two masses equals the mass of magnesium metal reacted. The magnesium should be accurately massed, because just as in Part 2, the amount of gas produced is determined by the mass of magnesium metal used.

3. Use a forceps to carefully place the solid reactant vessel within the reaction flask. The solid-reactant receiving vessel should float without a mixing of reactants. Be careful not to disturb the reaction vessel once the solid reactant container has been placed in the reaction flask; you do not want premature mixing of reactants. Do not seal it yet.

4. Follow the same procedures as outlined in steps in steps 8–21 of Part 1, above, and again in step 5 of Part 2, above.

5. Disassemble the apparatus and clean up.

Calculations

Part 1. Molar Volume of Oxygen (O_2) Gas

1. Determine the density of the 3% hydrogen peroxide solution by first subtracting the tare mass recorded in Part 1, step 3 from the gross mass recorded in Part 1, step 4 of the Methods section. Subsequently divide this net mass by the volume 5.0 mL.

2. Determine the moles of O_2 produced theoretically using the density of the hydrogen peroxide solution and assuming the solution contains 3% H_2O_2. Equation (9.9) shows the calculation. If using the alternate method, subtract the mass of the reaction flask with stopper, glass tube, and reactant vessel after the reaction (from step 20 of Part 1) from the mass of the reaction flask with stopper, glass tube, and reactant vessel before the reaction (from step 7 of Part 1). This is the mass of oxygen produced. Use the molar mass of molecular oxygen to determine the moles of molecular oxygen produced.

$$\text{moles } O_2 = (30.0 \text{ mL } H_2O_2 \text{ soln.})\left(\frac{g\, H_2O_2 \text{ soln}}{mL}\right)\left(\frac{3\, g\, H_2O_2}{100\, g\, H_2O_2 \text{ soln}}\right)$$

$$\left(\frac{1\, mol\, H_2O_2}{34\, g\, H_2O_2}\right)\left(\frac{0.5\, mol\, O_2}{1\, mol\, H_2O_2}\right) \tag{9.9}$$

3. Determine the average absolute temperature, K, of the reaction using equation (9.10).

$$\left[\frac{(T \text{ reaction flask} + T \text{ displacement flask})}{2}\right] + 273.15 \tag{9.10}$$

4. Determine the partial pressure of O_2 in the flask, P_{gas}, using equation (9.6). P_{H2O} is the vapor pressure of water, which can be obtained from the CRC Handbook of Chemistry.

5. Determine the volume of O_2 at STP, V_2, using equation (9.8).

6. Determine the molar volume of O_2 by dividing V_2 by the number of moles of O_2 determined in step 2, above, i.e., use equation (9.2). Express the result in Liters.

Part 2. Molar Volume of Carbon Dioxide (CO_2) Gas

1. Determine the moles of CO_2 produced theoretically using equation (9.11).

$$\text{(mass of NaHCO}_3)\left(\frac{1\,\text{mol NaHCO}_3}{?\,\text{g NaHCO}_3}\right)\left(\frac{?\,\text{mol CO}_2}{?\,\text{mol NaHCO}_3}\right) \tag{9.11}$$

2. Determine the average absolute temperature, K, of the reaction using equation (9.10).

3. Determine the partial pressure of CO_2 in the flask, P_{gas}, using equation (9.6). P_{H2O} is the vapor pressure of water, which can be obtained from the CRC Handbook of Chemistry and Physics.

4. Determine the volume of CO_2 at STP, V_2, using equation (9.8).

5. Determine the molar volume of CO_2 by dividing V_2 by the number of moles of CO_2 determined in step 1, above, i.e., use equation (9.2). Express the result in Liters.

Part 3. Molar Volume of Hydrogen (H_2) Gas

1. Determine the moles of H_2 produced theoretically using equation (9.12)

$$\text{(mass of Mg(s))}\left(\frac{1\,\text{mol Mg}}{?\,\text{g Mg}}\right)\left(\frac{?\,\text{mol H}_2}{?\,\text{mol Mg}}\right) \tag{9.12}$$

2. Determine the average absolute temperature, K, of the reaction using equation (9.10).

3. Determine the partial pressure of H_2 in the flask, P_{gas}, using equation (9.6). P_{H2O} is the vapor pressure of water, which can be obtained from the CRC Handbook of Chemistry and Physics.

4. Determine the volume of H_2 at STP, V_2, using equation (9.8).

5. Determine the molar volume of H_2 by dividing V_2 by the number of moles of H_2 determined in step 1, above, i.e., use equation (9.2). Express the result in Liters.

Percent Relative Error

Determine the percent relative error for O_2, CO_2, and H_2 gases using equation (9.13).

$$\%\ \text{Relative error} = \frac{\text{measured molar volume} - \text{ideal molar volume}}{\text{ideal molar volume}} \times 100 \tag{9.13}$$

For most common gases, molar volumes typically do not deviate more than ca. 1% from the ideal volume when atmospheric pressure is close to 1 atm.[2]

Deviation from Ideality—Real Gas Behavior

All real gases deviate to some extent from the behavior of ideality, where gas volume and intermolecular attractions are assumed negligible. Calculate the density (g L^{-1}) under standard conditions of each of the gases in this laboratory using equation (9.14), where M is molar mass in g mol^{-1}.

$$\text{density, } \rho = \frac{PM}{RT} \tag{9.14}$$

From the calculated density and exact molar masses, determine the molar volume of each gas, in liters, to five significant figures by dividing the molar mass by the gas density.

Results

Summarize your results by tabulating: (1) the moles of each gas reacted, (2) the volume of each gas produced under experimental conditions, (3) the volume of each gas produced under standard conditions, (4) the molar volume of each gas, and (5) the percent relative errors.

Discussion/Conclusions

Interpret your results and relate them to the objectives of the experiment. Focus your discussion on the meaning of your findings, not to recapitulate them. Discuss possible sources of error and/or explanations for deviation from the expected value of 22.414 L at STP. Based on your deviation from ideality calculations, which gas deviates the least? Which gas deviates the most? Explain these differences in terms of molar mass, molecular size, and bond polarity.

Your conclusions should include the molar volumes of the three gases and comments on the results in light of Avogadro's Law.

REFERENCES

The opening image was excerpted from Flowers, P.; Theopold, K.; Langley, R.; Robinson, W. *Chemistry*, OpenStax College. 2017. (https://openstax.org/details/books/chemistry).

1. Flowers, P.; Theopold, K.; Langley, R.; Robinson, W. *Chemistry*, OpenStax College. 2019. (https://openstax.org/details/books/chemistry-2e).
2. Postma, J. M.; Roberts, J. L., Jr.; Hollenberg, J. L. *Chemistry in the Laboratory*. The Molar Volume of Dioxygen and Other Gases. W.H. Freeman and Company: New York, 2000.

APPENDIX 1: Notebook Example

Unknown # ⑥

010

EXPERIMENT 7   17 JANUARY 1997

Determination of Sodium by Ion Exchange

I. Summary/Purpose:

   This lab is designed to determine the concentration of sodium ion in a NaCl solution. The Na^+ will be determined indirectly by passing a measured portion of unknown solution through an a cation exchange resin containing an excess (−) charge as a result of $R-SO_3^-$. The resin will be protonated with HCl with the exchange Ion Complex yielding $R SO_3^- H^+$. Na^+ ions will exchange with H^+ in a 1:1 ratio, thus final concentration of H^+ will equal the concentration of Na^+. The principle reaction behind this exchange process is:

$$R SO_3^- H^+(s) + Na^+(aq) \rightleftharpoons (R SO_3^-) Na^+ (s) + H^+ (aq)$$

from HCl

Chloride does not exist because it it was washed out of the resin with demineralized H_2O.

Reference: Analytical Chem. Lab Manual; E.B
            Rosser, E.B. 1971. "Determination of Na^+ by Ion exchange. ANAL-047.
            Christian, 5th ed, 1994.

II. Procedure:

A. Preparing Exchange Column

1. Place small plug of glass wool wool in bottom of column (baret)

2. Place ≃ 10 gram of CE resin in 150 ml beaker. Add demineralized H_2O to beaker and stir to a slurry. Pour slurry into exchange column and allow to settle.

3. Pour 20ml of demineralized H_2O into column without disturbing the resin. Drain water into beaker making sure to leave a small quantity of H_2O above the resin in the column. Repeat this step 2 more times.

107

011

Procedures: Preparing exchange column cont.

4. Protonate the resin by slowly pouring 25 ml of 3M HCl into column. Drain off the bottom into beaker. Repeat 2 more times and discard the eluted HCl.

(margin: 1-2 drops per second)

5. Wash resin with 20 ml of demineralized H_2O to remove excess HCl and Cl^-. Use a test tube and collect the last 2 ml of ~~elute~~ eluate. Add 1 drop of 0.1M silver nitrate solution to test for precipitation. If precipitation forms, rinse column again. Continue rinsing until only a slight turbidity results from 1 ml 0.1M $AgNO_3$ in 2ml eluate. Leave some H_2O in column until exchange is to take place.

(margin: Buret #1 has a very slow leak. + added more than usual Dm H2O)

(margin right: FVS 1-17-97 4:42 PM)

B. Determine Na^+ Concentration

(margin: Resumed on 1-31-97 12:03PM)

1. Obtain sample of NaCl of unknown Concentration (≥ 0.1M) (#6)

(margin: FVS)

2. Pipet 25 ml of NaCl into a 250 ml volumetric flask. Be sure to rinse pipet with NaCl solution prior to Transferring the pipeted volume. Add DI H_2O to bottom of flask neck, stopper and invert 10X. Finish filling flask to volume, stopper and invert another 10X.

3. Pipet 50 ml of diluted NaCl solution into a clean 250-ml beaker. Again, be sure to rinse pipet with diluted solution prior to transferring pipeted volume.

4. Drain the existing DI H_2O from prepared column and immediately pour the measured NaCl through the column, collecting the eluate in a clean 250-ml Erlenmeyer flask. Rinse the beaker with 25 ml of DI H_2O and pass it through the column. Do this 2 more times for a total of 3X. Collect all rinses in E. Flask.

(margin: 1-2 ml per gut. N.)

5. Repeat steps 3 and 4 4X. That is, do four determinations

(margin: Stopped 1-31-97 FVS)

6. Clean a 50 ml buret and rinse with 10ml of 0.01M NaOH Discard solution through tip.

012

Procedures: Determine Na⁺ Concentration cont.

7. Fill buret with 0.01M NaOH and discard small amount through tip (remove air bubbles). Record initial buret reading.

8. Add 3 drops of phenolphthalein to 4 flasks and titrate

9. Titrate until a slight pink color persists for 10 sec. after 1 drop has been added. Record final buret reading.

10. Two results should agree to 10 ppt or 1%

11. Calculate molarity of Na⁺, M Na⁺ in diluted samples 1 – 4.

$$M_{Na^+} = \frac{(M\ NaOH)(V\ NaOH)}{50\ ml} \tag{7.1}$$

where M = Molarity and V = Volume

12. Calculate $\bar{X}$ average M Na⁺ and finally, calculate M Na⁺ in original sample.

$$M = (10)(\bar{X}\ M_{Na^+}) \tag{7.2}$$

where 10 is the factor of $\frac{250\ ml}{25\ ml}$

III. Data

Sample Number ⑥   M of NaOH 0.09377 M ~~0.010~~

Determination	1	2	3	4
Final buret reading, ml	7.23	12.25	17.29	22.32
Initial buret reading, ml	2.19	7.23	12.28	17.29
Volume of NaOH used, ml	5.04	5.02	5.01	5.03

Finished experiment 2-7-97

$$M_{Na^+} = \frac{(M_{base})(V_{base})}{50.00\,ml}$$

IV. Calculations

1. Molarity of Na^+ in diluted unknown sample: eq. 7.1

[NaOH] was mislabeled. Needed to standardize. See Observation note p. 14.

Trial 1: $\dfrac{\overset{0.09377}{(\cancel{0.010})}(5.04\,ml)}{50\,ml}$ = $\overset{0.0095}{\cancel{0.00101}}$

Trial 2: $\dfrac{\overset{0.09379}{(\cancel{0.010})}(5.02\,ml)}{50\,ml}$ = $\overset{0.0094}{\cancel{0.00100}}$

Trial 3: $\dfrac{\overset{0.09377}{(\cancel{0.010})}(5.01\,ml)}{50\,ml}$ = $\overset{0.0094}{\cancel{0.00100}}$

Trial 4: $\dfrac{\overset{0.09377}{(\cancel{0.010})}(5.03\,ml)}{50\,ml}$ = $\overset{0.0094}{\cancel{0.00101}}$

$\bar{x} = \overset{0.0094}{\cancel{0.00100}}$

$\Delta = 0.00005$

2. Molarity of Na^+ in original sample: eq. 7.2

$$m = (10)(\bar{x}M_{Na^+}) = (\overset{0.0094}{\cancel{0.00100}})(10) = \boxed{\overset{0.094}{\cancel{0.0100}}}$$

3. Grams of Na^+ in original Sample:

$$\overset{0.094}{\cancel{0.010}}\,\frac{mmol}{ml}\quad 22.98\,\frac{mg}{mmol} = \boxed{\cancel{0.23\,mg/ml}}$$

$$\boxed{2.16\,\frac{mg}{ml}}$$

V. Results and Discussions

Table 7.1. Summary of results for Na^+ determination by exchange

Trial #	Buret Reading f	Buret Read yi	Vol used, ml	M Diluted	M original
1	7.23 ml	$\overset{2.19}{\cancel{12.25}}$ ml	5.04	$\overset{0.0095}{\cancel{0.00101}}$	
2	12.25	7.23	5.02	$\overset{0.0094}{\cancel{0.00100}}$	
3	17.29	12.28	5.01	$\overset{0.0094}{\cancel{0.00100}}$	
4	22.32	17.29	5.03	$\overset{0.0094}{\cancel{0.00101}}$	
Average	—	—	—	$\overset{0.0094}{\cancel{0.00100}}$	$\overset{0.094}{\cancel{0.0100}}$

Grams of $Na^+ = \cancel{0.23\,\frac{mg}{ml}} = \cancel{0.23\,g/L}$

$$\boxed{2.16\,mg/ml}$$

Results & Discussions cont.

<u>014</u>

Observation

note: The Molarity of the NaOH was marked
incorrectly. The bottle was labeled 0.010 M NaOH;
however, after standardizing, the true Molarity
turned out to be 0.0937. Consequently,
my original values were off by a factor of 10. I
made the necessary corrections.

2-14-97

<u>Standardization of NaOH</u>

<u>0.3401 g KHP</u>   Diluted to 100ml; 25 ml aliquot.

<u>Buret Readings</u>

	I	II
Final	7.80	12.23
initial	3.35	7.80
Vol, ml	4.45	4.43	$\bar{X} = 4.44$ ml NaOH

$$\frac{0.3401\,g\,KHP}{204.22\,g/mol} = \left(\frac{0.001665\,mol\,KHP}{0.1\,L}\right)(0.025\,L) = 0.0004163\ mol = equivalents$$

$$\frac{0.0004163\,mol}{0.00444\,L} = \boxed{0.09376\ M\ NaOH}$$

015

VI. Conclusions

Sodium ion concentration was determined indirectly by passing a known vol of an unknown NaCl solution through a protonated Cation exchange column. Average Na⁺ Concentration in original sample was 0.094 M. This is equivalent to 2.16 mg/ml of Na⁺.

This lab made me realize how critical it is to standardize the NaOH. In this lab, the NaOH was mislabeled and was off by a factor of 10 (see note).

2-14-97

Jack Schill

APPENDIX 2: Common Laboratory Equipment

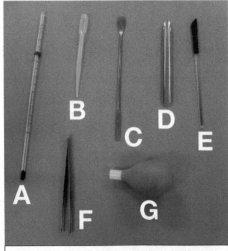

Thermometer (A), plastic transfer pipet (B), spatula (C), scoopula (D), stir rod and rubber policemen (E), forceps (F), and pipet bulb (G)

Polyethylene wash bottle

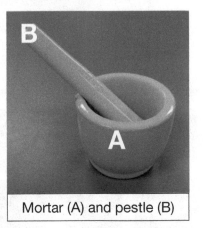

Mortar (A) and pestle (B)

Crucible and lid (A), evaporating dish (B)

Bunsen burner

Glass desiccator (A), metal desiccator (B)

Stir/hot plate with magnetic stir bar

Source: Frank Schindler

Pinch clamps

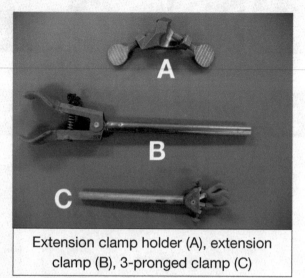

Extension clamp holder (A), extension clamp (B), 3-pronged clamp (C)

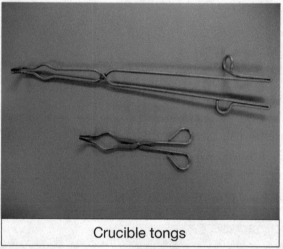

Crucible tongs

Electronic Analytical balance

Electronic Top-loading balance

Source: Frank Schindler

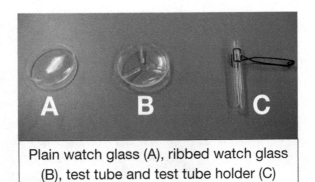

Plain watch glass (A), ribbed watch glass
(B), test tube and test tube holder (C)

Double buret holder
(A), buret (B), and buret
stand (C)

Ring stand (A),
ring with wire
gauze (B), ring
with clay or
ceramic
triangle (C),
and extension
clamp with
extension
clamp
holder (D)

Long and short stem
funnels

Source: Frank Schindler

Mohr pipet

Volumetric pipet

Volumetric flask

Erlenmeyer flask

Graduated cylinder

Beaker

Cuvette

Büchner funnel (A) and vacuum flask (B)

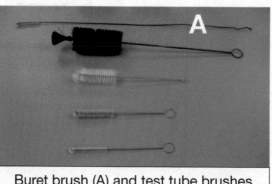

Buret brush (A) and test tube brushes

Source: Frank Schindler

Periodic Table of the Elements

Atomic Number → | 1 |
H | ← Symbol
Name → | Hydrogen 1.008 | ← Atomic Weight

1 IA																	18 VIIIA
1 H Hydrogen 1.008	**2 IIA**											**13 IIIA**	**14 IVA**	**15 VA**	**16 VIA**	**17 VIIA**	**2 He** Helium 4.002802
3 Li Lithium 6.94	**4 Be** Beryllium 9.0121831											**5 B** Boron 10.81	**6 C** Carbon 12.011	**7 N** Nitrogen 14.007	**8 O** Oxygen 15.999	**9 F** Fluorine 18.998403163	**10 Ne** Neon 20.1797
11 Na Sodium 22.98976928	**12 Mg** Magnesium 24.305	**3 IIIB**	**4 IVB**	**5 VB**	**6 VIB**	**7 VIIB**	**8 VIIIB**	**9 VIIIB**	**10 VIIIB**	**11 IB**	**12 IIB**	**13 Al** Aluminium 26.9815385	**14 Si** Silicon 28.085	**15 P** Phosphorus 30.973761998	**16 S** Sulfur 32.06	**17 Cl** Chlorine 35.45	**18 Ar** Argon 39.948
19 K Potassium 39.0983	**20 Ca** Calcium 40.078	**21 Sc** Scandium 44.955908	**22 Ti** Titanium 47.867	**23 V** Vanadium 50.9415	**24 Cr** Chromium 51.9961	**25 Mn** Manganese 54.938044	**26 Fe** Iron 55.845	**27 Co** Cobalt 58.933194	**28 Ni** Nickel 58.6934	**29 Cu** Copper 63.546	**30 Zn** Zinc 65.38	**31 Ga** Gallium 69.723	**32 Ge** Germanium 72.630	**33 As** Arsenic 74.921595	**34 Se** Selenium 78.971	**35 Br** Bromine 79.904	**36 Kr** Krypton 83.798
37 Rb Rubidium 85.4678	**38 Sr** Strontium 87.62	**39 Y** Yttrium 88.90584	**40 Zr** Zirconium 91.224	**41 Nb** Niobium 92.90637	**42 Mo** Molybdenum 95.95	**43 Tc** Technetium (98)	**44 Ru** Ruthenium 101.07	**45 Rh** Rhodium 102.90550	**46 Pd** Palladium 106.42	**47 Ag** Silver 107.8682	**48 Cd** Cadmium 112.414	**49 In** Indium 114.818	**50 Sn** Tin 118.710	**51 Sb** Antimony 121.760	**52 Te** Tellurium 127.60	**53 I** Iodine 126.90447	**54 Xe** Xenon 131.293
55 Cs Caesium 132.90545196	**56 Ba** Barium 137.327	57 - 71 Lanthanoids	**72 Hf** Hafnium 178.49	**73 Ta** Tantalum 180.94788	**74 W** Tungsten 183.84	**75 Re** Rhenium 186.207	**76 Os** Osmium 190.23	**77 Ir** Iridium 192.217	**78 Pt** Platinum 195.084	**79 Au** Gold 196.966569	**80 Hg** Mercury 200.592	**81 Tl** Thallium 204.38	**82 Pb** Lead 207.2	**83 Bi** Bismuth 208.98040	**84 Po** Polonium (209)	**85 At** Astatine (210)	**86 Rn** Radon (222)
87 Fr Francium (223)	**88 Ra** Radium (226)	89 - 103 Actinoids	**104 Rf** Rutherfordium (267)	**105 Db** Dubnium (268)	**106 Sg** Seaborgium (269)	**107 Bh** Bohrium (270)	**108 Hs** Hassium (269)	**109 Mt** Meitnerium (278)	**110 Ds** Darmstadtium (281)	**111 Rg** Roentgenium (282)	**112 Cn** Copernicium (285)	**113 Nh** Nihonium (286)	**114 Fl** Flerovium (289)	**115 Mc** Moscovium (289)	**116 Lv** Livermorium (293)	**117 Ts** Tennessine (294)	**118 Og** Oganesson (294)

57 La Lanthanum 138.90547	**58 Ce** Cerium 140.116	**59 Pr** Praseodymium 140.90766	**60 Nd** Neodymium 144.242	**61 Pm** Promethium (145)	**62 Sm** Samarium 150.36	**63 Eu** Europium 151.964	**64 Gd** Gadolinium 157.25	**65 Tb** Terbium 158.92535	**66 Dy** Dysprosium 162.500	**67 Ho** Holmium 164.93033	**68 Er** Erbium 167.259	**69 Tm** Thulium 168.93422	**70 Yb** Ytterbium 173.045	**71 Lu** Lutetium 174.9668
89 Ac Actinium (227)	**90 Th** Thorium 232.0377	**91 Pa** Protactinium 231.03588	**92 U** Uranium 238.02891	**93 Np** Neptunium (237)	**94 Pu** Plutonium (344)	**95 Am** Americium (243)	**96 Cm** Curium (247)	**97 Bk** Berkelium (247)	**98 Cf** Californium (251)	**99 Es** Einsteinium (252)	**100 Fm** Fermium (257)	**101 Md** Mendelevium (258)	**102 No** Nobelium (259)	**103 Lr** Lawrencium (266)

© Humdan/Shutterstock.com